By: Elijah Green

Creation Science Evangelism, Inc.
Copyright © 2008 Kent Hovind All Rights Reserved. Published 2008
Written by Dr. Kent Hovind
ISBN 978-1-944010-01-0

Printed in the United States of America
Distributed by Creation Science Evangelism, Inc.
For more information visit 2peter3.com or drdino.com

# The Kennel

## <u>Who On Earth Is Elijah Green?</u>

Actually I hope, and pray, and think it is safe now, seven years after the fact, to reveal that "Elijah Green" is a pseudonym for me, Kent Hovind. Let me explain:

The prophet Elijah was a famous man of God in the Bible. The king hated him and sought to kill him because he preached the truth boldly, and exposed the corruption in the kingdom and the sins of the king and queen (See I Kings 17 through II Kings 2). Evil men and women have always hated honest, bold, outspoken men of God who simply do their job. They can't handle the truth! John 3:19-20 tells us that evil men fear the light. Scores of Bible examples from Abel in Genesis, to Jesus, to John in Revelation show that evil men persecute good men. I've been a child of God since February 9th, 1969; an ordained Baptist preacher since May 25th, 1974; a high school science and math teacher for 15 years; a creation science evangelist since 1989; and an innocent man in the huge Federal Prison System since November 2nd, 2006 (see details on http://www.2peter3.com and http://www.FreeKentHovind.com – Released July 8, 2015).

Since I strive to understand and boldly and openly preach the truth of God's Word and I often expose the evil, corruption, lies (or just stupidity), of things that happen in our schools and government, I have made some powerful enemies too. Hence, the pseudonym: "Elijah."

---

**By Elijah Green**

# The Kennel

At the federal prison camp in Edgefield, South Carolina, where I was in 2008 when I wrote The Kennel, we wore green. Hence; the name: "Elijah Green."

I am completely embarrassed by the fact that even though I have been a serious student of the Bible for 46 years now, I completely missed the obvious fact that God's perfect Word (see Psalm 12:6-7 and Psalm 19:7) never authorizes prisons at all! I had to come to one to see this simple truth. Under God's law, criminals were given either a fine (Exodus 22), or a beating (Deuteronomy 25), or executed (Exodus 21), depending on the crime. Only the heathen nations around Israel had prisons, and God's people often suffered in them like Joseph, Jeremiah, Daniel, Peter, Paul, and many others. For nearly 40 years of my Christian life I was guilty of crying "tough on crime!" and advocated the unscriptural and cruel American prison system. I was guilty of calling for long prison terms for criminals. I now see how insane and wrong this is. We are punishing the wrong people! Long prison terms are tough on families and all Americans who are forced to pay for this bloated, cruel, senseless, and ineffective system.

Truly, our judges and prosecutors give out "burdens grievous to be borne", just as Jesus said in Matthew 23:4. I'm sorry, God. I've seen the light and will now help shine the light and make noise like Gideon's 300 did in Judges 7. Please join me. For this study, "Elijah Green" is an average, middle-aged man out for a drive in the country, when he accidentally finds something that changes his course and philosophy of life. Forever. I pray it will change yours too. Just as Harriet Beecher

By Elijah Green

# The Kennel

Stowe's classic book *Uncle Tom's Cabin* opened people's eyes to the insanity of American slavery in the 1800's, and as George Orwell's 1946 story *Animal Farm* showed the evils of Communism, I pray that *The Kennel* will sound an alarm and expose the evil (all for money of course, it always is, see I Timothy 6:10) of our American prison industrial complex.  Please share this story with others before it's too late.

By Elijah Green

# The Kennel

## <u>CHAPTER 1: The Discovery</u>

If I had not seen it with my own eyes and heard it with my own ears, I would not have believed it. It was almost like a bad dream, only it was real. I never imagined such a place could exist in a free country. This story is so bizarre that if you were telling me, I would not believe you. Nevertheless, I was there. All I can do is relate what I saw and heard, and let you decide.

I never would have noticed the place if I hadn't slowed down for the cow crossing the road. Actually, I had to stop and wait, while she stood right in the middle of that little-traveled country road and looked at me with that blank, non-thinking stare that only cows can give. While I waited for her to slowly chew her cud and contemplate her options about what to do next, I happened to notice a reflection from a glimmering object among the trees way off, maybe two hundred yards, to my left.

As I turned and focused, I realized it was a large area, enclosed with a real tall chain link fence topped with shiny razor wire, obviously where the reflection had come from. What? Why? Who? It made no sense. Well, Bessie finally discovered there was no grass in the middle of the road and slowly moseyed off into the field, but I just sat there trying to get my eyes and brain to agree on what I was seeing over in the woods.

---

5

By Elijah Green

# The Kennel

Why would anyone build such a huge, fenced-in place crowned with razor wire? And why way out here in the middle of nowhere? What or who are they (whoever "they" are) keeping in (or is it out of) there? Nothing about it made sense. So being curious and mostly uninhibited by nature, I turned and slowly drove down the long, narrow drive and stopped in front of the very large gate, which was also capped with shiny razor wire.

There over the top of the gate in giant letters was a sign that should have satisfied, but actually only intensified my curiosity. It read, "State Kennel of Middletown".

I unconsciously turned off the radio and rolled down the window, as if that would help me read it better, and that's when I heard it --- hundreds, and I mean hundreds, of dogs. They were barking, yelping, and howling in the most pitiful, heart-ripping sound I had ever heard. Immediately, it brought tears to my eyes. Why would anyone lock up all these dogs? Didn't they have a home to protect them somewhere? Weren't some children out there who would love them, pet them, and run around in the grass with them? Grass? It hit me. I saw lots of concrete, steel, and razor wire, but hardly any grass. It made no sense to me at all. Why were so many dogs locked up in there?

Now don't get me wrong. I know that some dogs are vicious and dangerous and need a place like this, but this place was huge! Could all these dogs be vicious and dangerous? What could it all mean?

6

**By Elijah Green**

# The Kennel

I was still trying to process all the sights, sounds, thoughts, and now smells, when a nicely dressed man opened the gate and walked up to my car.

"Hi," he said. "I'm John Cox, the kennel keeper. May I help you?" On his suit coat, top pocket was a professional-looking nametag that read: "John Cox - Kennel Keeper," so I knew he was serious about who he was.

Still slightly confused, I smiled weakly and said, "Hi, my name is Elijah Green. I was just passing by and saw the fence. I have never noticed this place before. What is it? What do you do here?"

Mr. Cox seemed pleased with my interest --- almost as if he were eager to show off his kingdom --- and said, "This is the newest, most advanced, state-of-the-art kennel for convicted dogs in the state. What type of work do you do, Mr. Green?"

"I've worked at Springfield Hardware for the past eight years."

"My, you are a ways from home! Would you like a tour of the kennel?" Mr. Cox asked. Well, being really curious now, and totally unable to comprehend who, what, or why, I quickly said,

"Sure! That would be wonderful!" Mr. Cox looked pleased.

"We don't get many visitors way out here. Park your car over there by my black Porsche and I'll show you around."

---

By Elijah Green

# The Kennel

Thus begins the story that no one will ever believe, but it's true. I was there.

**By Elijah Green**

## **CHAPTER 2: Behind the Gate**

Mr. Cox and I walked through the massive gate. It slowly closed on its own and made a heavy, almost sickening, mechanical "thud" as it automatically locked behind us. I cannot explain the feeling of panic, dread, or hopelessness that suddenly came over me as I heard that sound and actually felt the ground shake a little. You would have to have been there to understand. It was eerie. I was nearly overcome with claustrophobia and I was just inside the fence! I shuddered.

Anyway, Mr. Cox seemed eager to tell me everything, sort of like a kid with a new toy.

"This is the newest and largest kennel for convicted dogs in the state," he bragged. "There are just over 1600 dogs in here and we run it with a staff of only twenty-five."

"Sixteen hundred!" I exclaimed. "Why so many?"

"Oh, no," he corrected me. "The question is why so few? There are over two million dogs in our state and only fourteen kennels like this. This is only one of ten kennels operated by the state. The other four are privately owned by ICC, Incarcerated Canines Corporation, operating under state contract. At present, there are six large companies, and several smaller ones, which have gone into the private kennel business."

---

**By Elijah Green**

# The Kennel

Interrupting him I asked, "Who owns ICC and those other private kennel companies?"

"They are mostly owned by rich folks and senators. The founder of ICC was the former chairman of the Republican Party in Tennessee and friend of the governor. In fact, the governor's wife was a substantial investor in ICC, as was the speaker of the Tennessee House. Even some judges are shareholders. One of their larger stockholders was recently appointed by the President to be a trial judge in Tennessee. They say he has been in the courtroom as a lawyer on only two cases. Some of the families representing their dogs have had more courtroom experience than him.

"The other kennel companies do not operate in this state, so I do not know as much about them. However, we get a monthly magazine, The Kennel Monthly. Maybe you'd like a back issue. It has ads for the latest security devices available, as well as articles about some of the privately owned kennels. I do know that most of the private kennels are subsidized with tax dollars. In spite of our rapid growth, we can currently only hold one percent of the state's dogs. There are several thousand more dogs that have already been convicted and are on a waiting list to come in when we get space. The waiting list is so long in California, their Kennel Officers Association has proposed building a few mega-kennels that can hold up to 20,000 dogs each. Our country has the largest kennel system in the world, by far," he announced proudly as we walked past rows of cages.

By Elijah Green

# The Kennel

I struggled to imagine what it must be like to be one of these dogs locked in a really small cage!

"Mr. Cox, if there are fourteen kennels in this state, how many kennels like this are there in the country?"

"There are well over 900 kennels nationwide," he boasted. "This country has only 5% of the world's dog population," he continued, "yet 25% of the world's incarcerated dogs are in our kennels, proof that our country is the safest place to live. There are now over two million dogs in kennels like this across the country. Just seventy years ago, there was only one kennel in the state and it only had 300 dogs. But Congress passed new laws making more things a crime, and judges have been giving longer sentences. The kennel population has increased by over 700% in just the last forty years. For female dogs, the incarceration rate has risen 1200% since 1970. State law requires us to have forty square feet of space for each dog so we are licensed to house 1200 dogs in here."

"But I thought you said there were 1600 dogs here now," I said in a questioning manner.

Mr. Cox looked a little puzzled and said, "There are."

"Well, I don't understand. Doesn't that break the law and overcrowd the dogs?" I asked.

---

By Elijah Green

# The Kennel

He thought for a brief moment and said, "It does overcrowd them some but hey, they are just dogs. As for breaking the law, it actually doesn't. In a money saving effort, Congress has authorized us to be overcrowded by 37%. The kennels in California operate at 200% capacity. You see, we are allowed to put in an extra 250 dogs if it is on a temporary basis. That is if their dog blanket is not attached by Velcro to the floor. The law allows for that."

"How long is temporary?" I inquired.

"The law does not specify a time limit," he replied as we slowly walked past hundreds of cages of sad looking dogs begging for attention! "All kennels take advantage of this loophole in the law and are overcrowded, but hey, they are just dogs."

"Oh, I see," I stated almost mechanically, "What about the other 150?"

"Let's walk over to the SHED." He smiled as we veered off to the right and walked to the corner of the compound. "This will explain the other 150."

---

**By Elijah Green**

## **CHAPTER 3: The Shed**

"Wow! These cages are even tinier," I said as we approached, "and there sure are a lot of them. What is this area?"

"This is the SHED," he replied as he pointed to the sign and read, "'Special Housing to Educate Dogs." The dogs in here are being educated."

I stared at the sign and then at the dogs and said, "I don't understand. It looks like they are being deprived of everything. They don't have room to run around. They are isolated and cannot interact with other dogs. I don't see any toys for them to play with. They can't even see the sun or the sky from their cages. How does this educate them?"

He waved his hand slowly toward the cages and answered, "These dogs either broke kennel rules or are under investigation to see if they broke a rule. Depriving them helps educate them to obey the rules of the kennel."

My stomach knotted up as I thought of the poor dogs locked up in there. "How long do you keep them in there?" I asked.

"By law we can only keep them in here for 90 days. However, if we don't have space in the regular kennel, we take them out for 10 minutes and then we can legally put them back in for another 90 days."

---

13

**By Elijah Green**

# The Kennel

"I can't imagine what 6 months locked up in that tiny cage would do to a dog. Do they ever get out for exercise?" I asked.

"Oh, yes," he said. "By law we have to let them out into that bigger 20' x 20' cage for one hour each day, five days a week. It's a real nuisance to our staff though, so we try to schedule the exercise time early in the morning when it is cold and fewer dogs want to go. Plus, we can always cancel if it's raining or we are short on staff that day."

"Hello, Esau," Mr. Cox said with a slightly sarcastic tone to the dog on our left.

"Esau?" I inquired. "That's an unusual name for a dog."

"Mr. Green, Esau is not the dog's name. It's an acronym, which describes this dog. It stands for Extra Stupid and Ugly. Regardless of how many times we beat and discipline this dog, he will not learn. He'll be back in the SHED not long after he gets out."

It seemed awfully cruel to me to hear him make fun of the dog that was totally at his mercy at the moment. My mind quickly recalled scores of examples from history where prisoners were treated cruelly by captors "just because they could." I decided not to say anything about it and asked instead, "Do the dogs get good food in here?"

"Oh yes!" Mr. Cox beamed. "All dogs in the kennel get a well balanced diet, annual checkups by the staff vet, and dog biscuits every Christmas and Easter. They get a bath once a month and a new flea

By Elijah Green

# The Kennel

collar every 90 days.  Even the dogs in the SHED get that.  Although we try to keep the kennel clean, possibly 70% of the dogs will be carrying an infectious disease when they are released.  Dogs that are really sick are often released early to save money, so it's rare for a dog to die in here.

"Our staff vet does his best, however, some dogs just do not respond well to some of the drug therapy provided."

"Speaking of money," I replied, "who pays for the medical when you release the sick dog and who pays for all this? It must cost a fortune to run this kennel."

"Oh it costs a bundle all right.  That's the beauty of it.  The dog's owner is responsible for the sick dog's vet bills once he's out.  The taxpayers and the dog's family in the state foot the bill for the operational expenses of the kennel.  It's all part of the state budget.  We charge $20 per day for each dog.  If we spend it all we can justify asking for more next year," Mr. Cox answered.

"Twenty dollars a day!" I exclaimed.  "That's $600/month, over $7000/year times 1600 dogs..."  My mind raced...  "That's over 11 million dollars a year! The state could pay to send a person to college for less than what it costs to keep one dog in here."

"Actually it's more because we charge $25/day for each dog in the SHED.  So our budget last year was close to 12 million dollars," Mr. Cox

**By Elijah Green**

# The Kennel

said smiling. "And you're right about the college. My son just graduated from Middletown Community College. His tuition and books for the year was about $5000.

"Over the past twenty years, funding for incarcerating dogs has increased by 127%, while funding on higher education has increased by only 21%. We also get a pretty healthy sum of money from the National Veterinarians' Association each year," he said proudly.

By Elijah Green

## CHAPTER 4: The Experiments

"What's this about the National Veterinarians' Association?" I asked slowly and almost mechanically, as I was lost in thought. I could not see any good reason why they would give money to a kennel. I was thinking through all the who's, what's, and why's my mind could come up with, and finally, the words almost fell out of my mouth before I could even think to stop them: "Why would the NVA give money to a kennel?"

"Oh, they do lots of medical experiments with our dogs," he boasted. "Since we have so many in one location, they can test new drugs in the food and experiment with new procedures right here. It saves lots of money and red tape for the NVA. Currently, an estimated 45,000 researchers are conducting experiments in more than 10,000 programs. I don't know the statistics of how many dogs are involved. The United States is the only country in the world to officially sanction the use of incarcerated animals in experimental clinical trials. Even the CIA is involved in various mind control experiments. The Nuremberg Code of 1947 was drafted in direct response to the barbarity of the Nazi-era medical experiments on Jews, but Mr. Green, these are just dogs, so it's okay. It's exciting to know that the dogs they experiment with here may save some human lives in the future.

"At another kennel, several years ago they did experiments irradiating the dogs' reproductive organs and were able to reduce

By Elijah Green

# The Kennel

fertility rates to near zero.  That will save thousands of unwanted puppies from being born."

"Do the dogs or their owners know these experiments are going on?" I asked.

"I don't know," he said with a slight cock of his head and a quizzical look.  "I'm sure the NVA does everything the law requires.  I don't think it's anything to be concerned about.  After all, they're just dogs."

*Maybe to you they are just dogs*, I thought to myself, *but I bet they are more than that to their families.*

"This tour can be an educational experience for you, Mr. Green.  Something you should pass on to your children is the importance of keeping their dogs under control."

I had a gut feeling that this tour was going to give me more of an education than I ever dreamed.  "Mr. Cox," I said, "you told me that you had twenty-five staff here.  Do they get paid well?"

"Oh yes!  State jobs offer great benefits," he said.  "They get full medical, dental, life insurance and lots of state holidays off with pay, plus three weeks paid vacation.  The lowest paying jobs are the kennel cleaners.  They start at about $30,000 per year.  Everyone working here at least 20 years gets full retirement benefits at age 57.  The privately owned kennels do not pay nearly as well unless you are a cage broker."

By Elijah Green

# The Kennel

"That's sizeable pay for an entry level job!" I replied. "What do the top people make?"

"Oh, I think the top executives in the Bureau of Kennels start at about $150,000 per year," he said.

"It sounds like these jobs pay better than what I make. Mr. Cox, how do I get the job here?"

"Sorry, but you can't, Mr. Green. You're too old."

"What?" I demanded! "I am only forty-one and am obviously younger than you are, Mr. Cox. Besides, there are laws that protect against age discrimination."

"Yeah, but Congress makes exceptions to the laws for us because we deal with vicious animals. Even the Attorney General approved these exceptions. I've been working for the B.O.K. for a long time and will retire in two years. So, Mr. Green, unless you are a veterinarian, you can't be hired for these jobs, not even as a secretary. They don't want an older workforce here. In fact, we have a mandatory retirement at age 57. So if I don't like retirement, maybe I can come work for you, Mr. Green."

"The Attorney General does not have the right to approve exceptions to the law," I stated emphatically.

By Elijah Green

# The Kennel

"All I know is he did, Mr. Green, and that he decides which laws they will prosecute. I am not in a position to question such matters."

By Elijah Green

# The Kennel

## CHAPTER 5: Cage Brokers

"Mr. Cox, you mentioned a cage broker a moment ago. If I may ask, what does he do?"

"He is responsible for seeing that the private kennels are full. His commission can be as much as $5.50 per dog per day. States with overcrowded kennels can send dogs across country to be incarcerated in a private kennel. The county commissioners where the private kennel is located love it because the county also receives about $1.50 per dog per day. After a judge recently ordered relief from the overcrowding, one private kennel received 1200 new dogs in just one month. But back to our budget: in addition to salaries and benefits, we have to pay for all the dog food, utilities, maintenance of the kennel and lease payment for the property."

I was starting to feel that something fishy was going on so I asked, "Commissions? Lease payment? Who owns the property?"

Without flinching, and even a little cocky it seemed to me, Mr. Cox said, "This land belongs to a state senator. We have a hundred-year lease. Our lease payment is $10,000/month. Other senators, judges, and prosecutors lease property to other kennels or own companies that supply food, blankets, dog collars, or utilities.

"What's to stop the cage broker from bribing the judge to order relief of the overcrowding? I mean, if the commissions can be up to

21

By Elijah Green

# The Kennel

$37 per dog per week, the cage broker could be making over $40,000 per week just on that one event of the kennel receiving 1200 dogs."

"Mr. Green, judges are selected because of their character being above reproach. I'm certain that when the judge ordered relief from overcrowding, he did so for the benefit of the dogs. Now, if you'll follow me around to the back of the property, you can see some of our dogs at work. The work they do has become vital to our country.

"Some senators, and even some judges, profit from the work being performed by some of the dogs. Dogs doing work are attached by a leash and required to rotate the tread wheel, similar to big mill grinders used by local farmers that turn theirs with a mule. It just requires more dogs than it would mules. Or the dog can be forced to do other types of labor, such as pulling a plow for crops or any type work the expensive mules do. Often, the dogs have to be teamed together, with multiple teams of dogs to pull skids, wagons, plows, et cetera. Anything the expensive mules do, we can do here with enough dogs. Many of the grains, which the military uses, are ground up in kennels like this one.

"The kennel company NICOR, which stands for Nationally Institutionalized Canine Operational Resources, did not have to compete for government contracts until recently. In reality, the only way a company could compete with NICOR would be to use foreign imports, which we both know is bad for the economy.

---

By Elijah Green

# The Kennel

"Even worse, Congress is now allowing the military to do sole source purchasing of supplies from Iraq and Afghanistan. This will exclude other companies, including NICOR, from being the suppliers of these products, which the military was purchasing from NICOR. This is just another example of our government sending jobs out of the country.

"Mr. Green, the cost of operating the Kennel goes on regardless, and NICOR shares a small percentage of their profits with the Kennel. These dogs should have to work to help pay for their upkeep. The largest complaint against NICOR comes from businesses that use the expensive mules and cannot compete with the dogs. The government taxes the work done by the mules, but dogs working within the kennel industries are not taxed. In addition, the ASHA rules the government established for animal safety and health do not apply to incarcerated dogs and the kennel industries."

"Do all the dogs work?" I asked.

"In the old days, most of them had to, but now NICOR cannot expand quick enough to work all the dogs. After all, it is quite a large pool of free labor we have here. The private kennels are diversifying, finding other ways to work their dogs."

"Wow! That's quite a setup," I said. "I would guess that the senators really want to see this place stay full. Don't they?"

"It works out well for almost everyone," Mr. Cox said as he smiled.

---

23

By Elijah Green

# The Kennel

"The senate passes the laws, the *Department of Dog Catchers (DoDC)* enforces the laws by arresting dogs that break the laws, and the Animal Court determines how long the dogs will be sentenced to stay in the kennel. They are allowed a jury trial, but because most families do not know their country's history and *few jurors know about jury nullification,* they often just plead guilty. The sentences are worse if they try to fight it and lose. If we have too many empty spaces, the judges give out longer sentences or the senate can pass new laws to be sure we stay at full capacity. The news media cooperates with us as well. Every time a violent dog is arrested they put the story on TV and in the paper, telling how we are making the state a safer place by taking vicious and dangerous dogs off the street. This keeps the taxpayers feeling good about spending all this money."

By Elijah Green

# The Kennel

## CHAPTER 6: The High Cost

"Mr. Cox, I have to admit I haven't heard about jury nullification either. Can you tell me about it?"

"There is a lot about it on the internet. The jury or even just one juror, has the right to vote 'Not Guilty' to nullify bad laws. Most jurors have no clue about their real power. It's no surprise that you do not know, Mr. Green. The Department of Education has worked hard to remove this bit of history from school texts, just as they have to remove from history books how Christianity influenced the founding fathers of this country.

"Mr. Green, jurors have the power to nullify a law that they believe to be immoral, unconstitutional, or wrongly applied to the accused simply by returning a verdict of 'Not Guilty', regardless of their belief of guilt of the charged violation. Even a *Chief Justice* has affirmed this right of jurors. It has been an important part of American history, from refusing to return guilty verdicts against dogs that violated English law, practicing nullification in cases against individuals accused of harboring runaway dogs, and also those accused of violating laws during *Prohibition*. History tells of hundreds of bad or stupid laws that needed to be repealed."

My tour today was waking me up. I couldn't help thinking that a few people were profiting from all this while the taxpayers paid the bill and thousands of dogs suffered and kids at home cried themselves

By Elijah Green

# The Kennel

to sleep. "Does your $12 million budget include the cost of operating the *DoDC* and the Animal Court?" I asked.

"Oh, no," he said. "They have their own budget, but I don't know the numbers. The taxpayers foot the bill for them as well. The only financial connection with us would be the bonus we pay."

"Bonus?" I asked. "For what?"

Mr. Cox scratched his chin and said, "I don't know if it is called a bonus or a fee. It's really sort of an incentive. We pay $250 to the *DoDC* for each dog they bring in. That helps to motivate them to enforce the laws, and helps us meet our budget."

"Motivate? Incentive? Bonus?" I exclaimed, "It sounds more like a bounty to me! What would keep them from becoming too 'motivated' or even planting evidence and arresting innocent dogs just to collect the 'incentive'?"

Mr. Cox stared off into space as he thought. Finally he said, "Since they are all employees of the state and have taken an oath to defend and support the Constitution, everyone just trusts them to be honest and not be overzealous. We feel sure they stay within the law."

The whole picture was slowly forming in my gradually clearing mind. Determined to understand and get to the real root of why this place existed, I was beginning to see that it was a giant business and had little to do with locking up vicious or dangerous dogs.

---

By Elijah Green

# The Kennel

"Oh! Back to the news media," Mr. Cox said as if he just remembered it. "If a dog is vicious and bites or kills a human or another dog, they play the story over and over on the news and sometimes even make Hollywood movies about it. It's a shame that only 3% of the arrests are of vicious dogs. The public loves those stories of dogs killing innocent people! Ratings go way up when they are aired. There is even a top rated show about dogs that need to be caught. It's called *"The States' Most Wanted Dogs"*. The *DoDC* gets hundreds of anonymous tips after that show plays."

"Mr. Cox, has the media ever done a story about this place?" I asked.

"Oh yes, when we get a dangerous dog, we release that info to the media. They'll do a story about it."

"No, I meant has the media done a story about the operation of the kennel?"

"Mr. Green, while the BOK has a policy which seems media friendly, the Senate passed laws restricting their access. I would not have offered to give you a tour had you stated you work with the media. The Senate is afraid that if someone sees the dog that bit them on TV, it might traumatize them. They are also concerned that if the animal rights' groups see videos of the kennels that they would cause problems."

**By Elijah Green**

# The Kennel

"Or see the sham money making racket this place really is and shut it down!" I thought to myself.

"Mr. Cox," I began, "you said there was an Animal Court. How does that work?"

Mr. Cox said, "Let's walk over to my office where we can be more comfortable and answer your questions."

As we walked he spoke. "The Animal Court, well…. when a dog is caught by the *Department of Dog Catchers*, they go before the *Animal Court* to determine if they are guilty. Once they are found guilty, and 98% are, the judge issues a sentence based on the guidelines for the offense."

"What are typical offenses that dogs get sent here for?" I asked.

By Elijah Green

# The Kennel

## <u>CHAPTER 7: "The Crimes"</u>

Mr. Cox opened the door to his plush office, buzzed the secretary to bring in two Cokes, and said, "I have a copy of the guidelines right here in my desk. Let me find it for you."

While he was looking through his files, I gazed around the office. On the wall behind the huge mahogany desk were several diplomas and certificates. One said: "Associate Degree in Kennel Management". Another said: "Bachelors of Science in Dog Psychology". The room must have been well insulated because I could no longer hear the sad sounds of the lonely dogs calling for their families. I didn't know if my mind and heart could absorb much more, but the 'guidelines' provided another jolt to my system.

### OFFENSES:

"Ah, here they are in this book on page 316," he said as he handed me the book. "As you can see there are eight major categories that send dogs here plus a few dozen minor ones that are very rarely enforced."

By Elijah Green

# The Kennel

I slowly read the list aloud...

---

| | | |
|---|---|---|
| I. | <u>Biting another Dog or Human:</u> | (1-3 Months) |
| II. | <u>Killing a Human:</u> | (2-4 Months) |
| III. | <u>Killing another Dog:</u> | (3-6 Months) |
| IV. | <u>Running without a Leash:</u> | (4-10 Months) |
| V. | <u>Barking After Midnight:</u> | (5-12 Months) |
| VI. | <u>Possession of a Leather Chew Toy:</u> | (10-18 Months) |
| VII. | <u>Possession of a Leather Chew Toy<br>w/ intent to distribute:</u> | (36 Months to LIFE) |
| VIII. | <u>Conspiracy:</u> | (16-24 Months) |

---

"Wow! That's quite a list," I remarked. "Since one human year equals about seven dog years, these sentences seem awfully long! Do they get any break at all if it is their first offense?"

Mr. Cox sipped his Coke. "In the old days the judge had leeway to go below the minimum or even give a warning for first timers and send them home. Possession of a leather chew toy was a habit the government originally sought to help the dog overcome. There was no minimum sentence. When the laws were passed which established mandatory minimum sentences, an overcrowding of the kennels resulted quickly. To relieve the overcrowding conditions, laws were passed which let the dogs be released early on goodtime behavior.

---

**By Elijah Green**

# The Kennel

This angered the judges and the *DoDC* to see the dog released early, so the judges started giving longer sentences."

"In most states," he continued, "a dog can still earn an early release if he obeys the kennel rules and works hard. However, there are states like Georgia, which do not allow sentences to be reduced for good behavior. Many states like Florida abolished parole under the term 'Truth in Sentencing' but still rewards good behavior up to a maximum of 15% of the sentence. Alabama offers the most good-time credit among the Southern Legislative Conference states awarding up to 75 days credit per 30 days served."

"Can the dog lose the good-time reward?" I asked.

"Sure he can," he replied. "If a dog fails to work, violates a kennel rule, or gets in trouble with another dog, he can forfeit all or part of the gained time."

**By Elijah Green**

## CHAPTER 8: Chew Toys?

"It seems to me," I said, "that dogs that violate #1 - 3 should be killed. After all, if they are truly vicious and dangerous animals, why should everyone be required to pay to lock them up, especially since you are not making any effort to reform or train them in any way? It would be better for everyone if they were "put down." The family could get another dog and move on with their life. The victims of the attack would get closure, and the citizens in the state wouldn't have to pay $7,000 per dog each year to feed and house them. #4 and #5 could be handled with a fine or a special collar, and rescinding the law could stop #6, #7, and #8. That would save billions of dollars. By the way, why do they give the sentences in months? Why not days or hours?"

Mr. Cox reflected a moment and said, "In the old days the judge often did that. Giving a 30-day or 60-day sentence sounds like a lot, but to say 1 or 2 months doesn't sound as bad. I think it makes it easier for the judge to give out more time without looking so bad."

"A thirty day sentence would still be a really terrible punishment for the dogs and even worse for the kids," I said. "I bet none of the judges or senators or *DoDC* have ever experienced being locked up for 30 hours or even 30 minutes. It's amazing how people get fooled by simple terms. If the guideline said: Barking After Midnight --- 200,000-500,000 minutes locked in a cage it would look so much worse. That's what it really is to the dog, you know, and to the poor family that

By Elijah Green

# The Kennel

misses their dog. It seems to me that this method of punishment does even more damage to innocent families and children than it does to the dog."

"That's probably true," he said. "But as for mercy and shorter sentences, not anymore, not since the great 6-11 invasion."

"What was the 6-11 invasion?" I asked.

"Oh, it was awful!" he exclaimed. "A pack of 25 wild dogs burst across the border into El Paso. It happened on June 11th. All of them were wild and vicious and carried several leather chew toys. They quickly spread out and blended in with the local dog population. Only seven were caught and only three pounds of chew toys recovered. The search lasted for months! It was all over the news. Since so many were still at large and posed such a threat, most people were more than willing to allow the Senate to pass emergency legislation that took away a few constitutional rights in exchange for peace and security. Because of the Wild Dog Act of 6-11, judges must get tougher on crime. They sentence all dogs based on the new guidelines. The days of parole, second chance and alternative punishment are gone. But as for killing a dog, we can't do that, Mr. Green. That would be cruelty to animals, and besides, it takes a while to train our dogs to work at NICOR. There are some who feel we should just exterminate the bad dogs and rid society of this tax burden, but there's no reason to let that training and free labor go to waste."

---

By Elijah Green

# The Kennel

"Are their statistics showing the ratio of male dogs to female dogs incarcerated? *Or black and white dogs*? Or how many of the Mexican Chihuahuas are in the kennel and how many dogs are in here for each offense?" I asked.

"About 93% of the dogs we keep are males. The female dogs are usually housed in a separate kennel. Most kennels have a lot more black dogs than white. At present, more than 10% of all young adult black male dogs are in kennels like this. It is estimated that in about fifteen years, at the current rate of growth, more than 50% of all adult black dogs in the country will be in kennels like this. I'm not sure why. I know there are some who believe that the black dogs are not as smart as other dogs. They feel good that the black dogs cannot breed, at least not while they are in here. But it could be that the *DoDC* has it out for them. You would have to ask them. I just lock up the ones they bring me.

"As for why they are here..... I'll show you." Mr. Cox pulled a list out of his drawer and said, "Well, we have twelve dogs here for #1 - biting; six for #2 - killing a human; four for #3 - killing a dog; and the rest for the last five offenses. The majority are here for #6 - #8, a little over 400 dogs for each."

I was nearly speechless as I looked at the list and heard the numbers he was reading. "There are 400 dogs in here for possession of a leather chew toy?"

By Elijah Green

# The Kennel

"412," he stated, "to be exact.  Plus another 420 for #7, so 832 total."

"I don't understand," I said.  "Over half of these dogs are here for this.  Isn't it natural for dogs to want to chew?  What is wrong with possessing a leather chew toy?  Plus, why should it cost the taxpayers thousands of dollars when a dog breaks the law?  Doesn't locking them up punish the wrong people?"

**By Elijah Green**

# The Kennel

## CHAPTER 9: Conspiracy?

Mr. Cox seemed a little surprised at my questions and replied, "I don't make the laws or enforce them. I just keep the dogs they bring me. I just follow orders."

"How did such a law ever get passed?" I asked.

"Mr. Green, in 1973, the governor of New York was very influential in promoting the long incarceration terms for dogs caught with the leather chew toys. He had high political aspirations and wanted to appear "tough on crime." He even became Vice-President the following year. Prior to the Governor making his inaugural speech, the incarceration rate was 110 per 100,000 dogs. During the 80's, the President declared a war on leather chew toys. Other politicians joined the bandwagon of being 'tough on crime' and it spread like wildfire across the nation. The right wing conservatives really pushed to elect candidates and judges who promised long prison terms. Some judge's even brag they will give out a million years while on the bench if they are elected. That's how they measure 'tough on crime' in their mind. Today, the incarceration rate is over 760 per 100,000. When you only count adult dogs, the rate is 1 per 100.38.

"There was a study done that showed some dogs get addicted to the flavor of leather chew toys and tend to want them for the rest of their lives. Some even think they might cause aggressive behavior, but no link was ever proven. Plastic chew toys are still fine. All I know is

---

By Elijah Green

# The Kennel

without that law and the conspiracy law, this place would be nearly empty and I'd have to lay off most of my staff. That would have a very negative financial impact on Middletown. It would be a ghost town. Why, my property value would plummet!"

"What is this #8 - conspiracy law about?" I asked.

"If I remember correctly," he said as he tapped his fingers on the desk, "the dog catchers' union lobbied for that one. They were having a really hard time catching enough dogs to keep up their BMW car payments. The dogs would hide their chew toys or run back in their yard when other dogs alerted them that the *DoDC* was coming. Under the new conspiracy laws, if any dog barks to alert another dog, helps hide chew toys, or even knows about another dog possessing a leather chew toy or breaking any other law, and doesn't cooperate with the *DoDC*, they can be arrested and charged with conspiracy. It makes it so easy for the *DoDC* to get convictions now."

"Do you mean they can arrest, convict, and lock up dogs on hearsay evidence without hard evidence or actually seeing the dog commit any violation?" I questioned. I immediately recalled what the Pope had said and realized the truth of it: "In a world without truth, freedom loses its foundation."

"In the old days there had to be hard evidence," he said as he sipped his Coke. "But convictions were truly hard to get and our kennel system was really small. Now, all the *DoDC* needs is any two

---

37

# The Kennel

dogs to testify against another dog to get a conviction. If the two dogs that testify happen to be locked up or headed to the kennel at the time, they will get time off their sentence."

"How do dogs testify?" I asked.

"By barking more than three times when they see the accused dog," he replied matter-of-factly. I thought for a moment.

"What's to prevent them from lying just to get their sentence reduced?"

Mr. Cox leaned back in his chair and got a slightly glazed look on his eyes as he stared at the back wall. "They take an oath to tell the truth and the judges in the Animal Court can tell when they are lying. That's why they are called 'judges', you know. We know the system works because the *DoDC* has a 98% conviction rate."

"Mr. Cox, I can't help but feel that this conspiracy law is against everything this great country of ours was founded on. Why, those two dogs might never have met or even seen the accused dog in their lives. They could make up the whole story. It would amount to guilty till proven innocent. It makes it extremely easy for any dog to be arrested for conspiracy. Then the family would face huge legal bills just to defend their dog. The courts and lawyers would love that law because of the income it generates for them, but it seems so unfair for the poor families and dogs! I also can't see any difference between

By Elijah Green

# The Kennel

offering time off sentences to dogs that testify against other dogs and bribing a witness. That is so wrong! You have over 400 dogs in here on 'conspiracy' charges. Doesn't that seem wrong to you?"

He appeared to actually be thinking for a moment and then said, "There are 437 dogs, to be exact, in here for conspiracy. If we sent them all home we could never meet the budget. Plus, I don't make the laws. *I just follow orders*."

**By Elijah Green**

## **CHAPTER 10: Conviction Rate**

I was stunned at this information. I heard a small voice in me saying that there was a real big fundamental problem here. I felt like I was starting out on "the Yellow Brick Road" --- a money trail that would lead me to a strange place. Could the 98% conviction rate be because most people cannot afford to defend themselves against the government?

I wondered to myself, could it be because all lawyers, even defense attorneys, swear to make their first loyalty to the court and not their client? Could it be because the *DoDC* attorneys, dog catchers, and witnesses are allowed to lie on the witness stand, plant evidence, entrap people and their dogs, and even infiltrate or influence juries, and the judges not only allow it but seem to encourage it?

Could it be because the average juror automatically believes "their government" would never lie and the "accused must be guilty" since, "after all, they were arrested"? Could the 98% conviction rate be because the *DoDC* has learned that by charging 20 or 30 or even 100 counts, the jurors will be influenced to believe "there must be guilt somewhere" and convict on at least a few counts? After all, if you throw enough mud, some of it is bound to stick somewhere, even if only in the minds of the jurors!

Could it be because the jurors went to a school that no longer teaches the truth about jurors' rights to vote on both the facts and the

By Elijah Green

# The Kennel

law? Could it be because the judge lies to the jurors by telling them they cannot decide or even consider whether the law itself is fair or just? Could it be because the jury never sees the actual law, but only the judge's "instructions" about the law? Why doesn't the judge tell them the truth about jury nullification? Does anyone remember that Hitler and Stalin's courts had a 100% conviction rate but were still evil and wrong, and tens of millions of innocent people suffered and died?

My mind was racing again. I slowly focused on Mr. Cox's sincere, serene smile and asked, "Do the judges also get a bounty or bonus?"

Mr. Cox seemed a little shocked by that question. "Oh no!" That would prejudice the Court. Most of the power is in the hands of the *DoDC*. In fact, many of the judges used to work in the *DoDC*. There is no money exchanged that I know of, but the judges normally rule for the *DoDC* because they are afraid their own dog will be arrested. These judges have kids that love their dogs, too, you know. They wouldn't want to hear their kids cry at night."

"I see," I mumbled softly as I thought of the thousands of kids at home crying for their dog right that very moment. "Do any families ever challenge the Court's decision to try to keep their dog out of the kennel?

Mr. Cox pulled out another piece of paper, looked at it, and said, "Yes. Last year there were 2,707 convictions in Animal Court. Seven hundred of them were appealed, and only nine convictions were

By Elijah Green

# The Kennel

overturned on appeal.  The appeal typically costs $30,000 and lasts about 16 months.  During that time the dog stays in here."

"Boy! The sentence would be over by then for most offenses," I said.

"Yes," Mr. Cox acknowledged sadly.  "Justice moves slowly sometimes.  If a family takes the case to Court and loses, their dog will probably get the maximum sentence in the guidelines, while those who take a plea bargain get much less."

"Sir," I began slowly, "I cannot see what good is accomplished for the dog, the family, or society by locking these non-violent dogs up for long periods of time.  The Romans said 2,000 years ago that prolonged incarceration was 'cruel and unusual punishment'.  Do you have children, Mr. Cox?"

"Yes, I do," he said.  "My son is 28, and my daughter is 26."

"Did you always use the same punishment with them as they grew up?"

"What do you mean?" he asked.

"Well, when they were toddlers, I would suspect you used a simple thump on the hand when they disobeyed, and as preschoolers a seat in the corner or 'time out', and only used a paddle for serious or deliberate repeat offenses.  Didn't you?" I asked.

By Elijah Green

# The Kennel

"Yes, that is correct," he replied with a slight smile, as he remembered their childhood.

"It seems to me that over-use of the paddle would create bitterness. Imagine that you caught your son smoking a cigarette at age 12 and told him he was going to get 5 swats with the paddle every day for 16 months as punishment. What would his reaction have been?" I asked.

Mr. Cox looked surprised. "Why he would have hated me and said, 'Dad! Give it to me all at once. Get it over with. Please!'"

"Exactly!" I said. "That's my point. Locking up dogs or people for long time periods is just a long, protracted beating. It doesn't do any good and does great harm to all involved, especially to the children affected by it. It has to break up relationships between dogs and families in many cases. I think we should rethink this whole process. *First, should the laws exist, especially for categories #6 - #8?*

"For Pete's sake, just legalize the chew toys! Second, should the *DoDC* get rewarded for how many dogs they arrest and convict? How can a system like that not go corrupt? Third, is locking them up the only punishment available? Can't Congress think of other options? Other countries don't do this.

"Fourth, why would anyone want a mandatory minimum term for dogs, especially on their first offense? Do they not realize that the

By Elijah Green

# The Kennel

Law of the Lord is perfect, and in God's laws there are no provisions for incarceration? God's Word calls for beatings for some crimes (Deut. 25:3; Luke 12:47), restitution plus penalties for others (Exodus 22:1, 4; Leviticus 6:5), and execution for others (Exodus 19:13; Numbers 15:36). How can the senators and judges, who own stock in the kennels or one of the kennel industries, really remain objective, honest, and just, the way this is set up? How can this not be a clear case of conflict of interest?"

Mr. Cox looked at me with a far away stare that reminded me a little of the cow in the road. It appeared like he was trying to wrap his mind around a whole new thought, but it wouldn't stretch far enough.

After a moment of awkward silence he slowly said, "I have never thought of those things, Mr. Green. Those are very thought-provoking questions, but *I don't make the laws, I just follow orders*."

**By Elijah Green**

# The Kennel

## CHAPTER 11: The DoDC

I was trying to absorb the enormity of the problem and the pain this evil system inflicted, all for the love of money, when I heard a faint yelp down the hall. "I'd like to learn more about the *DoDC*," I said.

Mr. Cox had heard the yelp as well and turned to look down the hall. "Well, that's perfect timing. Here comes a *DoDC* staff member now. I'll introduce you and see if he has time to answer your questions."

I turned to look down the hall with Mr. Cox. There I saw a short, pudgy man pulling a reluctant and obviously terrified little puppy. The choke collar was attached to a leash that led through an eight-foot length of pipe so the puppy couldn't reach the dogcatcher to bite him. I could detect a faint, cocky smirk on the little man's face, he also had a stun gun, extra leash, mace, and a .45-caliber pistol, all strapped to a belt around and slightly under a roll where his waist should have been or used to be.

His neatly pressed uniform was straining at the lower buttons and had several large shiny badges pinned on it. The largest badge said, "*Department of Dog Catchers*". As I looked at his face I couldn't help but wonder if this wasn't the same guy I had seen two months ago working at the burger place on Main Street. I was trying to gather my thoughts and control my emotions as I looked down at the terrified little puppy tugging at the chain when Mr. Cox said, "Mr. Green, this is

---

45

# The Kennel

Hans Krause, the assistant dog catcher. I think he would be glad to answer a few questions."

I reached out and shook hands with Hans. His hand seemed sweaty, as if pulling that puppy down the hall was more exertion than he was used to doing. "Pleasure to meet you, Mr. Krause," I said. "Mr. Cox tells me you know a lot about the *DoDC*."

Hans straightened up, tried to suck in his stomach a little, smiled, and wiped a sleeve over his badges as he said, "I'd be glad to help you, Mr. Green. What would you like to know?"

Mr. Cox offered a Coke to Mr. Krause, which he quickly accepted. I sipped on mine and began by asking, "How many people work in the *DoDC*?"

Hans took a gulp of Coke as he pushed the pipe to the floor to force the puppy to lie down or choke, and then replied, "There are 12 in this district and 8 districts in the state, so about 100," he boasted.

"And what is required to get a job in the *DoDC*?" I asked.

From the quickness of his response I guessed that he knew because it had just recently happened to him. "Just a willingness to risk your life to make the state a safer place. They train you, but the training is not hard. We had to use five officers, a helicopter, tear gas, and break the fence down to apprehend this criminal. He had a chew toy and got twelve months," he said with a proud grin. "We learned about

By Elijah Green

# The Kennel

using excessive force in training.  It helps instill fear in the entire neighborhood, plus it is a real boost to our own ego."

"Hitler and Stalin would be pleased with how we have copied their methods," I whispered.  But I didn't say it loud enough for them to hear.  Mr. Cox handed Hans an envelope, which I assume contained his $250 "incentive" for bringing in this "dangerous animal".  As Hans slipped it in his pocket, I saw a slight smile grace his face.

*Well…. let's see…. the taxpayers get a bill for $7,000 to house this puppy for a year, more kids cry at home, Mr. Cox, and twenty four others are assured jobs, and Hans gets $250*, I thought.  So this is how a police state works.  Even the family that lost their puppy shares in the tax bill to lock him up.

I glanced down at the poor puppy still struggling at the choke collar, and before I knew it, my thoughts came out as words.  "Hans, do you ever feel guilty for taking dogs away from their families?" I asked.

The smile faded from his face and I wished I had not said anything, but it was too late now.  The question was out.  "I felt rotten the first few weeks," he said sadly, "but they say you get used to it.  It was really hard watching kids cry as I locked up their puppy, but hey, I don't make the laws.  I just do my job.  I just follow orders.

"I had nightmares for the first few weeks, and I still struggle some. I've got kids too, and a dog……… I just focus on doing my job to feed

**By Elijah Green**

# The Kennel

my family and pay my bills. I admit I do look forward to retiring though. I've only got 19 years and 11 months to go."

*Ah, it is the burger guy*, I thought, but this time I didn't say it out loud. "Hans, do any of the dogs you arrest have puppies of their own at home?" I asked.

Hans lowered his head and bit his lip for a moment before he replied, "Yes…… quite often they do. It takes nerves of steel for us to drag them away from their little ones."

He paused a moment and continued, "My nerves aren't steel yet but they say it comes with experience. I hope it comes soon for me," he sighed.

No one said anything for a moment. I pondered quietly that I was getting a glimpse of the real child abusers in America. Hans just looked down at the puppy and I saw his shoulders relax and sag a little, as if they carried a heavy load.

**By Elijah Green**

## CHAPTER 12: Senator Jones

Just then the intercom on Mr. Cox's desk interrupted the awkward silence. "Mr. Cox, Senator Jones is here. He needs to see you right away. He says it's urgent and will only take a moment."

"Send him in," Mr. Cox said in a voice that reflected a little pride or self-importance thought.

The senator entered wearing an expensive suit and politicians' smile. He reached across the desk to shake hands with Mr. Cox. Senator Jones smiled at Mr. Krause and I, and said to the kennel keeper, "I'm sorry to interrupt you gentlemen. This will only take a moment and I'm in a big hurry. There has been a simple mistake. My grandson's dog was accidentally picked up last night by the DC for possession of a leather chew toy."

He reached into his inside suit coat pocket and pulled out an envelope and said, "This letter will explain everything."

Mr. Cox accepted it with a slight nod, hefted it once for just an instant before slipping it into his own coat pocket and said, "I'm sorry for the mix-up, Senator. I'll have one of my men bring your grandson's dog up right away."

"Actually," Senator Jones began, "I'm really pressed for time. I'll just go get him, if you don't mind."

# The Kennel

My curious and uninhibited nature took hold again. Before I knew it I said, "Mr. Cox, I'd love to see the rest of the kennel and ask the Senator a few questions. May I go with him as he gets his dog?"

Mr. Cox thought for a brief second and answered, "We need to drop off this new arrival in the same area so let's just all walk together. You can finish the tour and get your questions answered all at the same time."

As we walked past hundreds of cages with dogs of all sizes and ages, most whining and begging to be petted and many were mere puppies, I introduced myself to Senator Jones and said, "Sir, I'm pretty confused about what I'm seeing today. Why did the Senate vote to outlaw leather chew toys? It seems to me like that's a natural thing for dogs to do and your law has created a crime over this. What does it hurt if they have leather chew toys?"

Senator Jones paused for a moment, as if he were about to give a political speech, and said, "For many years they were legal, and in many countries today they still are but there was a lot of political pressure put on us about 35 years ago to outlaw them. The animal rights activists were against them. They donated a lot of money to my campaign so, of course, I had to vote for their bill."

Once again my unrestrained personality dominated before I could stop it and I blurted, "Of course you did. The Bible explains all that in 1st Timothy 6:10."

---

**By Elijah Green**

# The Kennel

The senator looked both pleased and puzzled --- pleased that he could justify his actions with the Bible and that I had appeared to agree with him, and puzzled as if he were trying to remember what that verse said. He covered his ignorance, like a veteran politician, as he said, "Oh yes. The Bible. That's a great book. I always look to it to guide me in policies and decisions."

I couldn't resist the opening, "So, do you read the Bible often?"

"Oh yes, every day," he lied.

"Have you ever read the book of Hezekiah to see what he says about being kind to animals?" I asked, trying very hard not to smile or laugh, since there is no book of Hezekiah.

Without hesitation and with great political poise he said, "Many times. I was just reading it with my family yesterday. Great book! Oh, here's my grandson's dog. Come here, boy! Let's get you out of here and away from all these bad dogs. I hate to run gentlemen, but I have a committee meeting in two hours. We are considering changing the 'No Barking After Midnight' law."

Seeing a flicker of hope to change a silly law that has harmed hundreds of families and caused untold suffering unnecessarily I asked, "What are the proposed changes to the law?"

"We are considering moving the time to 11 p.m.," he said proudly.

**By Elijah Green**

# The Kennel

"Are you for the change?" I asked.

He straightened his shoulders and got a far-away look on his face as if he were thinking on a subject of great national security and said, "I've given it a great deal of consideration and I've had an enormous amount of input from my constituents on both sides of the issue. Seven said I should vote against the change and eleven have encouraged me to vote for it. I have to listen to the will of the people so I'll probably vote for it. Well gentlemen, I've got my grandson's dog and I must hurry."

"Senator," I interjected, "may I ask just one more quick question?"

He lovingly patted the dog's head and said, "Just a quick one."

"Has the Senate ever considered just dropping the no-barking law, conspiracy law, chew toy laws, and leash law altogether? A simple no-bark collar could solve the barking problem, and there are constitutional issues about the other laws. That would send nearly all these lonely dogs home to their loving families and help a lot of hurting kids, plus save the taxpayers billions of dollars," I said.

The senator looked stunned by my audacity to even suggest such a thing! He reacted, "What! If we did that, we would only have a few dozen dogs here that were violent. We could never meet the budget for the kennel. I would be forced to oppose any bill that would even attempt to do that."

---

By Elijah Green

# The Kennel

"Why?" I asked.

"Why? Because I own the land this kennel is built on. They could never afford the lease payment. Plus, that would cause great harm to many other segments of this massive business."

"Thanks for your time and answers, Senator Jones," Mr. Cox interrupted. "I'm sorry about the mistake with your grandson's dog. "Turning to me he said, "OK, Mr. Green, let's go across the aisle to put our new arrival in his cage.

**By Elijah Green**

## CHAPTER 13: Bonus Points?

As Hans dragged the still struggling puppy toward his new home, I first heard and then saw a very muscular pit bull growling at the puppy. The hair on the back of the pit bull was standing up and the puppy gave out a pitiful whine as he wet the floor.

Mr. Cox reached for the latch on the pit-bull's cage and said, "This is one of those four dogs we've got in here for killing another dog. He gets out in four months."

As Hans pushed the frantic puppy inside and released his collar I implored, "Won't the pit bull hurt this puppy?"

Mr. Cox glanced at the pit bull for a moment as the puppy quivered in the corner of the cage and said, "Oh I doubt it. If he does he will go to the SHED and it will add more time to his sentence. I feel bad, but this is the only cage we have room in right now. I wish the taxpayers would vote for that bill to construct more kennels. We sure need the space! Plus, my cousin needs a job."

As we turned away to continue the tour, the puppy gave the most heart-rending whine I had ever heard! Tears welled up in my eyes as I realized that this system was so well-entrenched there was nothing I could do for the puppy but pray for God to protect it. I hoped that four months of being locked up with that pit bull wouldn't take away his sweet innocence and make him grow up to be a vicious dog. But

By Elijah Green

# The Kennel

inside I knew the chances of this were slim and the kennel would probably have another "guest", or should I say "customer" a few months after this puppy is released, if he survives.

"Hans," I asked, "what 'crimes' does the *DoDC* spend most of their time on?"

Hans thought for a moment and answered, "Chew toys and conspiracy. I'd say that about 80% of our arrests are for those crimes. We wouldn't have much to do without those laws to enforce. I probably wouldn't have this job. Why, last year, the *DoDC* was able to arrest a pack of 15 dogs in one day! They had a huge smuggling ring going on, bringing in illegal chew toys from a neighboring state. These packs of dogs are getting better organized every year. They were real slick about it, but we caught them! Well, I mean, they caught them. I wasn't working for the *DoDC* at that time, although I sure wish I had been! That would have been awesome to be part of that sting operation. It was featured on the *States' Most Wanted Dogs*. The senior DoDC staff, still talk about it all the time. One was even bitten by one of the dogs when he tried to arrest him. He got a medical retirement with full benefits for life. Now, he plays golf almost every day."

Hans seemed to be reliving, and maybe embellishing, the story in his mind over and over as he stared off into space and smiled. He continued, "Boy, you should have heard the guys talking around the

---

**By Elijah Green**

# The Kennel

water cooler that day!  They tell me that one guy was bragging that he got nearly two hundred points from just that one raid!"

I had not heard of points before, so I asked, "What's a point, and what are they for?"

"Oh, it's sort of an off-the-record competition all the *DoDC* staff have," said Hans.  "Every time we make an arrest that results in a dog being incarcerated in a kennel, we get one point for each month of the sentence.  We all know that promotions within the DoDC are based on these points.  One guy in our office has earned over eight hundred thousand points over the last nineteen years.  He's trying to get over a million before he retires in four years.  He could retire next year, but I think he wants to set the record before they make him retire.  I sure hope he makes it.  That would be so cool to have the Captain talk about him at the retirement party!"

I choked back the lump forming in my throat and tried to stop the tears forming in my eyes as I thought about hundreds of thousands of lonely months this system was inflicting on both dogs and kids just so these guys could boast around a water cooler.  I blinked back the tears as I looked at Hans.  He was obviously dreaming of getting his own "points" for this poor puppy today.

Slowly he came back to the present, shook his head slightly --- as if to clear his mind --- and said, "Well gentlemen, I hate to rush off but I have an important job to do.  There are still vicious dogs out there to

By Elijah Green

# The Kennel

apprehend, and duty demands that I go protect the innocent people from dangerous animals.  After all, I took an oath to uphold the law. Good day, gentlemen."

As Hans walked off twirling his leash and whistling, Mr. Cox looked after him and sighed, "Where would our state be without brave men and women like him?"

*Yes indeed*, I thought, *where would we be?*

**By Elijah Green**

# The Kennel

## CHAPTER 14: Wasting Money

As we strolled past another row of cages, I noticed several water hoses had been left running full blast, apparently by the kennel cleaners. The hoses were lying on the concrete and the streams of water were each snaking their way toward a storm drain. I could see no kennel workers in the area and no reason for the waste.

As we approached one stream, Mr. Cox, who seemed totally unconcerned and maybe even oblivious to any problem, simply stepped over it to keep his shoes from getting wet and continued walking as if it was perfectly normal.

Having been responsible for paying my own utility bills for many years had caused me to notice things like this, even at other peoples' houses. I can't tell you how many times I had to remind my own children to shut the door or turn off the water or shut off the lights. I'm sure you understand if you have bills to pay. As I prepared to step over the stream myself, my curiosity got the best of me.

"Mr. Cox," I began, "shouldn't someone shut off that water? It seems like a waste of resources to let it run if they are done. Isn't it?"

He paused a moment, looked back at the water hoses producing the streams and then proceeded walking away and said, "Oh, the kennel cleaners will shut them off eventually. Don't worry about it. The more water we use here the better it is for the small local utility

By Elijah Green

# The Kennel

company. Our utility bills are pretty high here. It helps support the local economy. Plus, the more we spend, the more we can ask for next year in the annual budget increase. It works out great for everyone. Conservation of resources is not a big concern for us here. We are too busy keeping the state safe from dangerous animals."

I glanced back at the water pouring into the drain and had to stifle my conservative urge to run over and shut off the hoses myself. I looked at Mr. Cox, who was now two steps ahead of me, continuing the tour as if nothing had happened.

I couldn't bring myself to believe this is really happening. This whole kennel system is a deliberate waste of tax dollars. How could a place exist where waste is rewarded? Do other government agencies and employees develop the same warped thinking over time? I wondered. Was I still in my home country or had I somehow been transported to another planet in a dream and would soon wake up? The pitiful howl of a lonely puppy to my left snapped me back to reality. I wasn't dreaming.

"Mr. Cox," I said. "Do the children ever get to come and visit with their dogs?"

"Oh yes, after the dog has been here 30 days," he replied smiling. "Our policy states that our goal is to keep the bond between dogs and families strong. We allow them to visit twice a week for four hours each time in the visiting area over there. However, the State is

By Elijah Green

# The Kennel

considering legislation that will cut the visitation time in half as a means to reduce the kennel's budget. But during the first 30 days of incarceration the dog is not allowed any visitors. Some families drive 8 hours just to come see their dog. Sadly, many families just get another dog and their old dog is left here alone for us to take care of.

Unfortunately, the children rarely bond as well or enjoy the new dog as much. Usually, the children still want to come see their old dog, but they are rarely brought here. Hundreds of these dogs never get a visit. Apparently the families think that the bond with their new dog will get better by forgetting the old dog."

As we entered the small, drab, unfurnished visiting area I thought, *there is nothing to do in here for the dogs or the kids.* There were vending machines and chairs and a few tables and that was it. The prices on the vending machines caught my attention. "Two dollars for a Coke! Three dollars for juice! That's outrageous! Why would anyone pay that instead of just bringing their snacks with them?"

"Visitors are not allowed to bring food, Mr. Green. It's the policy of the Bureau of Kennels. As for the price, that's a benefit for the staff. Eighty-five percent of the profits go for staff recreation and fifteen percent goes to the BOK."

Then, what he had said earlier finally registered with me. "Eight hours!" I exclaimed without meaning to raise my voice. "If the state has fourteen kennels, I don't see how any dog can ever be locked up

---

60

**By Elijah Green**

# The Kennel

more than an hour's drive from its owner. Don't you put them in the kennel that is closest to their home?"

"Of course we do," he said somewhat defensively. "That is, if we have room. If the dogs cause trouble or break any kennel rules, we can move them across the state, or to another state, for punishment. Because of overcrowding, the dog can even be sent to a private kennel. However, if a dog is placed in a private kennel, he can be moved much farther away.

For example, many of the dogs from Hawaii are sent to Arizona or Kentucky. Dogs from Kansas may go to Florida. The cage broker helps find a place for them. Private companies now transport thousands of dogs across the United States. The dogs may spend as long as a month on the road on their way to a private kennel. There are more laws regulating the transporting of cattle than there are for transporting these dogs, Mr. Green. Just remember, if the owner had kept their dog under control, he wouldn't be here."

**By Elijah Green**

# The Kennel

## CHAPTER 15: Sick Puppy

"What kind of things could a dog do in here that would make you move him far from his family?" I asked.

"Oh, we have lots of rules in the kennel system," he said. "Moving their food or water dish, barking too loudly, scratching the fence or gate, or possessing a leather chew toy. " You know, things like that. Sometimes, rather than move them, we just take away their visiting rights as punishment. It's usually for only six or twelve months at a time. We have one dog over there in cage #738 that tried to dig under his fence to escape. We took away his visiting rights and dog biscuits for 24 months."

This was unbelievable! Why couldn't Mr. Cox realize how much permanent damage that particular punishment would do to both the dog and the family? Couldn't he understand that it would be natural for every dog to want to escape from this place --- not to go out and be dangerous, but to be back with a loving family?

"If a dog is sick, are the family members afforded any special visitation privileges?" I asked.

"Oh, no!" he exclaimed. "To the contrary, family members are not allowed to visit their dog in the animal hospital unless the dog is in critical condition, and then visitation is limited to only fifteen minutes."

By Elijah Green

# The Kennel

"Mr. Cox," I said, "of all the things you can do to punish dogs who violate rules, why would taking away their family visits even be on the list of options? That seems so cruel."

"Letting families come visit causes problems for us. Some kids know their puppy is teething so they sneak chew toys into the visiting area. Our staff even gets bribed to smuggle them in once in a while. It's a real problem in here and takes a lot of our staff time to monitor. But hey, I don't make the laws. I just do my job. I just follow orders."

I'd heard that before, but this time it sparked a question, so I asked, "Doesn't keeping these dogs locked up for long periods of time like this alienate them from their owners, and make them less playful and more aggressive when they do go home?"

Mr. Cox wrinkled his eyebrows in thought and said, "Probably. Maybe that's why over 90% of the dogs return to the kennel within a year of getting out. The BOK developed policies to try and reduce the rate of recidivism to no avail. The other problem is the label they all get. Any dog that has ever been locked up will be labeled a 'felon' for the rest of its life. He can't leave the state to go on family vacations, without going through a lot of red tape, and if he ever goes to the city pound because his family rejects him, he will probably be the last ones adopted out, if anyone will take him.

"Most of the dogs seem real friendly and well-trained when they come," he continued. "It's a real shame that 80% are abandoned by

---

By Elijah Green

# The Kennel

their families if they are here more than 10 months. The abandonment rate is even higher for female dogs. Unfortunately, the dogs are not allowed to develop new friendships with outsiders while they are here. The dogs are allowed visits only with people who knew them prior to their incarceration. If abandoned by their family, they are usually left here forgotten. It's the law. When they get out, without those relationships, they usually get into trouble quicker and end up back here. After they have been here for a while, they seem to change. They are less friendly and playful. Some even turn mean or even vicious. It's sad to see them get that way. Under the Three Strikes Law, dogs that are caught a third time for the same offense are classed as incorrigible and sentenced to life."

"Do the staff officers ever abuse the dogs?" I asked.

"It happens sometimes, when you're constantly around mean animals," he responded. "Congress passed laws to try to reduce it, but those laws do not apply to the privately owned kennels."

"Does the staff abuser get punished?"

"Mr. Green, most abuse is only considered to be a misdemeanor, not worth the trouble to charge them. Besides, the staff officers are like heroes in the eyes of the public, protecting society, and these are just dogs in here. Once, four guards were charged with the beating death of a female dog, but charges were dropped after they could not determine the time of her death. In Florida, two staff officers were

By Elijah Green

# The Kennel

acquitted for stomping a dog to death.  That dog must have really been mean."

*Or the staff members*, I thought.  "Do your staff members here ever show any affection to the dogs like petting them, brushing them, or talking nicely to them?" I asked.

"Many years ago the kennel did that sort of thing before the big change in philosophy," he replied.

---

65

**By Elijah Green**

## CHAPTER 16: Tough on Crime

"What change in philosophy?" I inquired.

"In the 1970s, the kennel system was commonly seen as a way to rehabilitate and prepare the offending dogs to be returned to their families, " he said matter-of-factly. "We told our staff to be as nice as they could be to the dogs and help them in any way we could because we felt that just being away from their home and family was punishment enough. We even had frequent training classes and allowed dogs to go home for weekend furloughs once a month. Then, about 25 years ago, the head of the Bureau of Kennels sent out a memo to all kennel keepers that the new philosophy was that dogs are here 'for' instead of 'as' punishment and that we were to look for ways to make them miserable so they would quit coming back. Nearly all training classes and furloughs stopped. I think the policy change came because of pressure from the right wing conservatives whose slogan was 'tough on crime'. They were a powerful political force. It got to the place where you couldn't get elected without their support.

"A few thought we had gotten too tough on crime. For instance, the media did not like it when one of the training videos for a private kennel showed a seemingly compliant dog being kicked and shocked with the stun gun, but these techniques can be useful in breaking a dog's rebellious spirit. I still do not know how they got to see that video."

---

**By Elijah Green**

# The Kennel

"Mr. Cox, does the staff members ever shoot the dogs?" I asked.

"Not here we don't... Our state doesn't allow it. But at the Red Onion Kennel in Virginia they do. But they only use rubber bullets inside the compound. During their first nine months, they shot over sixty dogs, injuring ten. That instilled a fear in the other dogs, which should keep them in line."

I was walking with him silently and thinking about all I had seen and heard when we came upon a kennel worker carrying a huge sack of dog food toward the open trunk of his car. Inside the trunk, there appeared to already be several sacks of dog food.

Mr. Cox quickly looked away, veered off slightly to the left, and began, "This is our own food preparation area. We provide well-balanced meals to keep the dogs healthy. It costs us about 85¢ a day to feed each dog."

"85¢ a day!" I exclaimed. "How can you provide enough food at such a low price?"

"Oh, it's very simple..." Mr. Cox smiled. "We get truck loads of food donated because it is past the expiration date. Very few of the FDA food laws apply to kennel food. Many of the other kennels are using private companies to feed the dogs. Using a private company to feed the dogs has created many problems. Several states now do this as a cost-saving measure, but lawmakers still want food costs reduced

---

By Elijah Green

# The Kennel

another 14%. When eating is perhaps the biggest pleasure in a dog's day, it's easy for fights to break out due to petty jealousies over food. There have been some problems with the private company in charge of feeding the dogs as well. They don't keep the food preparation area very clean, there have been some instances of maggots on the dogs' trays, and they have even been caught dipping spoiled meat in vinegar and water to remove the smell. Often they do not fix enough food for all of the dogs. When food portions are too small, a hungry dog can become a problem dog, but the state is saving money. Many companies send us outdated or slightly spoiled food, we get it for free and they can write the full retail value off on their taxes. It works out good for everyone."

"Everyone, except the dogs," I thought. "Doesn't that pose a health risk to the dogs?"

"Oh, maybe a little, but hey, they are just dogs. Besides, we have a long list of dogs already sentenced waiting to come here when we get space. We have no problem staying full."

I remembered back to my college history class where I learned how labeling people into groups make it easier to mistreat them. Communists labeled their opponents as "enemies of the state", Hitler labeled Jews as "inferior species" or "criminals" or "parasites", blacks were called lots of negative terms during slavery, the whites called the Indians "savages". The list was real long! And here I was today hearing

By Elijah Green

# The Kennel

"they are just dogs". I was beginning to see the true picture and plan. It wasn't pretty.

**By Elijah Green**

## CHAPTER 17: Staff "Benefits"

I was still having a hard time believing what I was hearing and seeing. *I must be dreaming*, I thought. This can't be really happening in my country, the one my brother and I fought for and thousands have died for. How could anyone with a conscience be part of such a scheme and still sleep at night? Do the taxpayers really know what is going on behind this fence way out here next to nowhere? How could I tell them? What could they do? It was obvious to everyone that something must be done to get truly dangerous or vicious dogs off the street, but 1600 dogs? 14 kennels in this state and over 900 kennels in the country? Chew toys? Conspiracy? 200,000,000 dogs? Has everyone gone stupid at once? My mind was racing in all directions when I remembered the open trunk.

"What happens if a dog steals extra food from the food preparation area?" I asked.

"Oh, that's a serious offense!" he said. "That dog would face new charges and get a longer sentence in the kennel, plus time in the SHED."

"Do they have to go back to the Animal Court to face the new charges?"

"Rarely, Mr. Green. Our staff usually gets to decide if the dog is guilty and what the punishment should be. We are trained for this,

# The Kennel

and the state trusts that our decisions will help keep the public safe from these vicious animals."

"Do the staff members ever steal food for their dogs at home?" I asked as I looked back at the kennel worker loading the last sack of food in his trunk.

"There may be some petty theft by our staff, but we sort of look the other way and consider it part of their benefits," he said. "After all, we are putting our lives on the line in here to protect the public from dangerous animals."

I thought of the hundreds of lonely dogs we had seen today whining and begging to be loved. Some were very old and could barely stand up in their cage. I would say that way less than 10% could be called "dangerous animals." Maybe years ago, when only dangerous animals were locked up, he would be correct to think of himself as a hero; but what I had seen today was mostly a huge money making business. My mind went back to the new puppy in with the pit bull and I silently prayed for him to somehow survive. I thought of all the hundreds of kids who were home crying right that minute because they missed their dog. I wondered how many more burglaries there were now because family watchdogs were locked up in here. As I thought back over the sights and sounds of the day, a tear welled up in my eye and trickled down my cheek.

---

By Elijah Green

# The Kennel

Mr. Cox saw it and said, "I know. I get emotional too as I think about the brave staff we have working here to make the state a safer place."

"Mr. Cox," I said, "what exactly are you trying to accomplish in the lives of these dogs and families? No other country on Earth does this to the extreme our country does. What does locking them up for seven months accomplish that they can't learn in seven days?"

"That's a great question," he said. "I don't know of any good that comes from this place except to provide a lot of jobs and take a few dangerous animals off the street. Local businesses benefit when families come to visit their dogs, as they often have to stay in the hotel and eat while they are in town. It also helps lots of local economies when the dog's time is up and he is released to the half-way house."

"The half-way house?" I asked. "What is that?"

"Oh, almost all dogs are required to go for 60 days to a half-way house so they can be gradually transitioned back into society. The owner pays the halfway house $10 per day for the sixty days. Most dogs are really allowed to go home after only ten days or so, but they must pay for all sixty days," Mr. Cox said. "Then they can bring in more dogs to fill the vacancies."

"Wow!" I said. "They could rent the same space out to six dogs. What a lucrative place that is!"

---

By Elijah Green

# The Kennel

"That's why it helps the local economy so much. There are scores of these half-way houses around the state," he said smiling. "The taxpayers don't pay for that. The dogs get regular jobs. No NICOR, etc."

**By Elijah Green**

## **CHAPTER 18: My Transformation**

I was stunned! I couldn't believe what I was hearing. "This whole system seems to me to be nothing but a giant money-making machine and lots of people are in on it," I said. "The welfare of the dog or the family is way down on the list, if it is even on it. Protecting the public from dangerous animals is only a smokescreen."

"You are probably right, Mr. Green. Money and politics intersect at Corruption Avenue. It's the nature of American politics. Even the Roman historian, Tacitus, stated back about 1900 years ago, "The more corrupt the state, the more numerous the laws." There's nothing we can do about it though, but do our job and pay taxes. I am both humbled and honored to have this job, knowing that I am helping keep our state safe from dangerous animals."

We were walking slowly toward the massive gate. Mr. Cox paused a moment and said, "Well, our tour is complete. I think you have seen everything we have here. Do you have any other questions?"

I looked at Mr. Cox. He seemed so professional, so methodical, and so mechanical. I wondered if he had any feelings of remorse for the suffering he was bringing to families and dogs. I wondered if he realized how many ways he could help ease that suffering. Couldn't he hear the same lonely whines I was hearing? Couldn't he see the dogs shaking in fear? Couldn't he understand why kids cried as they left the visiting area each week? Would he even consider the idea

---

74

# The Kennel

that the problem was not the dogs or the families, but the laws that criminalize innocent conduct? Did he lobby to eliminate the ludicrous laws that caused nearly all of these dogs to be here? Did he ever consider the idea that the problem could be solved some other cheaper way like fines or dog collars? Was it not evident that the love of money was causing most of this evil? How could he sleep at night?

Do the taxpayers realize that what had started as a legitimate place for a few vicious dogs had grown into such a huge business? Do they know that only a few of the dogs really needed to be in here, and most were here over dumb laws or because of a system that rewards the *DoDC* for convictions and not for seeking truth and justice? Everyone knows we need laws and crime should be punished, but this? Couldn't he see that most of these dogs should go home, now, today, to their families? Couldn't he hear the children cry at night? What was happening to my country? Has everyone gone crazy at once?

Did my countrymen see this fence as a good thing to prevent escape and never wonder why the dogs would want to escape? Couldn't America see --- to paraphrase from Uncle Tom's Cabin --- that this system was creating "anguish and despair, breaking thousands of hearts, shattering thousands of families, and driving helpless people to frenzy and despair? "Is this a thing to be defended, sympathized with, passed over in silence."

What happened to the liberty part of life --- liberty and the pursuit of happiness? Would it be a waste of time to even mention my

**By Elijah Green**

# The Kennel

thoughts to Mr. Cox, or Hans, or Senator Jones since they all made money off this kennel? The senate could fix nearly all of these problems in one day, but why would they? How could anyone convince them to vote to eliminate part of their own income, power and prestige? Has any politician in history ever done that? I could not think of any.

My mind was racing in all directions at once and all I could mutter was, "I don't have any more questions Mr. Cox. Thanks so much for your time."

Mr. Cox shook my hand and smiled as he opened the huge gate for me. It shut behind me with that same heavy, heartless, mechanical, ground-shaking thud. Even though I was now outside, I still had a sick feeling in my stomach. I used to be proud of my country, but visiting this place shook my faith in our justice system. I slowly drove out to the main road where Bessie had wandered back into the middle. I stopped and watched her mindlessly chewing her mouthful of grass and staring at me with that same blank, non-thinking stare that only cows can give. I'm sure she had no clue that she had changed my life forever. The sun was setting and I glanced over toward the kennel where I saw a tiny reflection off the razor wire. I just sat quietly and

By Elijah Green

# The Kennel

gazed at it for a long time, and I wept.

By Elijah Green

# The Kennel

## <u>Summary</u>

For centuries, the abuse of alcohol has created problems for the family. Some people believed that alcoholic beverages endangered mental and physical health. They also thought drunkenness helped some people commit crime. In 1917, Congress approved the *18th Amendment to the Constitution*, which prohibited the manufacture and sale of alcohol and took effect in 1920. Congress also passed the *Volstead Act*, which established penalties for prohibition violations. The results of *Prohibition* was not fewer people drinking, but more as people thought the law violated their right to live according to their own standards. Government grew bigger trying to enforce the laws and crime increased. Gangs provided most of the alcoholic beverages and warred with other gangs for control of the liquor trade. It took a while for Americans to realize that the *Prohibition laws* and the "war on alcohol" did more harm than good, so in 1933, Prohibition was repealed with the passage of the 21$^{\underline{st}}$ Amendment.

Now let us consider drugs and the effect of the war on drugs. Some people believe that drugs endanger mental and physical health. Some people also believe that drug use helps people commit crime. Yet for centuries, people have used and abused drugs. Drug use has not come down as a result of laws, but has increased, and along with it came an increase in crime, criminal activity, and gang violence. Possibly it is a rebel nature within man to want to do that which is forbidden, i.e. 56, or more, in a 55 speed limit zone. This book is not

By Elijah Green

intended to condone the use of drugs or alcohol, but to raise awareness that the laws which outlaw drugs are causing more harm than good to nearly everyone, and costing the taxpayers billions of dollars annually, not only to incarcerate the drug offenders, but also billions extra on enforcing these laws and in welfare to affected families. These laws need to be repealed, and many prisoners set free. It is also intended to highlight some of the problems with the prison system. There is evidence that releasing non-violent drug offenders would save money on corrections because the economic impact of their offending is so low.

If drug sales were restricted as is alcohol so that they may only be sold to person's age 21 and older, they could be sold at the convenient store along with cigarettes and alcohol. Then, what now sells for $20 because it is illegal would probably be less than $1. Instantly, the drug dealers would be out of business. The need to commit crime to support a $100 per day habit would be drastically reduced by the affordability. The $5 billion dollars the President promised one of the Central American countries for them to curtail their drug supply line would be saved as the incentive to export into the United States would be gone.

People who are now sniffing paint for a buzz and for fear of the law could get a safer and cheaper high. Drugs that require the use of a needle could be restricted, but motivation to use such would be drastically diminished by the availability of other drugs. 20% of the police department would not be needed and could find employment

By Elijah Green

doing something more useful. The Coast Guard and Border Patrol would no longer have to worry about drug smugglers since the market would no longer be profitable. Over 50% of the budget for incarceration could be saved. That savings could go a long way toward reducing the national debt, or just be money the taxpayers save.

---

*"Government exists to protect us from each other. Where government has gone beyond its limits is in deciding to protect us from ourselves." --Ronald Reagan.*

*"For nothing is more destructive of respect for the government and the law of the land than passing laws which cannot be enforced, it is an open secret that the dangerous increase of crime in this country is closely connected with this."--Albert Einstein.*

*"Totalitarianism is when people believe they can punish their way to perfection." --Newt Gingrich.*

*"Penalties against possession of a drug should not be more damaging to an individual than the use of the drug itself." --Jimmy Carter.*

---

**By Elijah Green**

# The Kennel

From as early as 1912 the U.S. has tried to export its domestic drug policy and forced other countries to emulate it even though it has been anything but a model of success. This could be one reason much of the world hates the U.S. as their crime rate and prison population also increase.

Suicide rates are higher among families which have a family member incarcerated, as are divorce rates. People imprisoned are twice as likely to be abusive after being released.

Largely, through jury nullification, prohibition was repealed, and the crimes associated with prohibition ceased. It is time to end the war on drugs. If a person is going to do drugs, experience has shown that they will regardless of the law, and some will because of the laws against it. Why should the taxpayer reward them with free housing? Consider the following:

## "Words of the Founding Fathers" Concerning Jury Nullification

*"Jurors should acquit, even against the judge's instruction... if exercising their judgment with discretion and honesty they have a clear conviction the charge of the court is wrong."* --Alexander Hamilton, 1804

*"It is not only the juror's right, but his duty to find the verdict according to his own best understanding, judgment and conscience,*

---

By Elijah Green

***though in direct opposition to the instruction of the court." --John*** *Adams, 1771*

***"I consider trial by jury as the only anchor yet imagined by man by which a government can be held to the principles of its constitution."*** *--Thomas Jefferson, 1789*

---------------------------------------------------------------------------------------------

If you are called for jury duty, know your rights and responsibilities. You can go to www.fija.org for more information. FIJA stands for Fully Informed Jury Association.

## Costs of Incarceration:

But wait a minute! Is it actually free housing for the inmate? If the inmate is classed at above the poverty level, and the court has not exempted the inmate, the state can take from his assets the costs of incarceration (which range from $28 per day to $165 per day or $10,000-$60,000 per inmate per year), the court costs, and the cost of prosecuting him until his assets are reduced to the poverty level. Federal prisons only collect costs of incarceration, which can be over $23,000 per year.

While incarcerated, an inmate is not eligible for Medicare or Medicaid, but may be charged for his medical care.

By Elijah Green

# The Kennel

*Liens* against retirement income may be assessed and the state can take any inheritance he receives up to twenty years after being released.  The fourteenth Amendment, which prohibits the government from seizing property without due process of law, doesn't really count in the eyes of the court when it comes to prisons.  A prison having a policy of seizing the assets is considered "due process."  Prisons can even implement a retroactive policy to make the inmate pay it.  You're thinking to yourself, "No way!  They can't do that, not in the United States!"  But it is happening.

### Get on the computer and go right now to:
http://www.aele.org/law/2008JBAPR/2008-4MLJ301.pdf and read some of the case summaries where it has been done.  Remember, Hitler financed much of his war machine with assets he seized from Jews.

While furloughs are supposed to be granted to non-violent inmates who are within two years of being released, they will not be granted if the inmate does not sign the financial responsibility form agreeing to pay for the costs of his incarceration.  In addition, the parole Commission will be notified of the inmate's "failure to participate".  The inmate will not receive performance pay above the maintenance pay level, nor will the inmate be assigned to any work detail outside the secure perimeter of the facility.  The inmate will not be allowed to work in UNICOR (UNICOR is the prison industry for federal prisoners.  Each state has a prison industry for state inmates.)  The list goes on and on.

---

83

By Elijah Green

# The Kennel

If the inmate works at UNICOR, or one of the other prison industries, he/she can feel good that the OSHA (Occupational Safety Health Administration) rules, which companies are required to comply with to minimize the risk of injury to the employee, do not apply. If he/she is injured while working within the prison industries, around the prison facilities, or whatever job the prison finds for the inmate, since they are not considered employees of the state, they are not covered by workman's compensation. But if they were (rules in some states may), and they receive a compensation award for an injury, the state may take a large part of it to cover the costs of incarceration. This also applies if an inmate was injured prior to, or after, incarceration, any compensation award may be apprehended.

Regular gifts from family or friends to an inmate may also be seized. It is important to note here that unless the judge waived the fine, or imposed a fine (which could be as low as $0), which included the cost of incarceration, assets may be taken from the inmate until he has been reduced to poverty level. If the inmate was convicted of crimes prior to November 1st, 1987 and is still in prison, he is referred to as an "Old Law Inmate" and the rules are slightly different. "An inmate held on the sole basis of his/her inability to pay such fine, or fine and costs, AND whose non-exempt property does not exceed $20 may request a discharge from imprisonment on the basis of indigence (see 18 U.S.C. § 3569)" He will not be classed at indigent level if he receives regular gifts from family or friends, which means they can take up to 85% of a regular gift. State laws vary on this. But, unless the inmate was

By Elijah Green

# The Kennel

wealthy prior to incarceration, he/she stands a large chance of leaving at poverty level. Could this be a plan to eliminate the middle class citizen? Vending machine prices in the visitor area are higher than machines elsewhere. Telephone rates are higher than elsewhere, and since the calls are often collect calls to family, it adds to the financial burden of family and friends of inmates. It is estimated that inmate calls generate a billion dollars or more in revenues each year. A prison typically receives 30-40% of all telephone revenue. If an inmate calls home and the child picks up on the extension phone to also talk and listen to dad/mom, that's against the law. The inmate can be disciplined by having phone privileges taken away for several months, including spending time in the Hole, S.H.U. (Special Housing Unit) isolation.

If the inmate received a federal or state felony conviction for possession, use or distribution of a controlled substance that the individual committed after August 22nd, 1996 he/she is ineligible for food stamps. So, not only do we reduce them to poverty, the government removes most of the assistance granted to help Americans in time of need.

Inmates at a halfway house are expected to be employed 40 hours per week within fifteen calendar days after their arrival. During their stay, they are required to pay a subsistence fee to help defray the cost of their confinement. This charge is 25% of their gross income, not to exceed the average daily cost of their placement into the halfway house.

85

By Elijah Green

# How much does it cost to build a prison?

South Carolina's estimate of construction in 2012 dollars by facility type are: $147,000 per bed in a maximum security institution; $95,300 per bed in a high security facility; $89,200 per bed in medium security; and $47,000 per bed in a minimum security housing. Results of Incarceration: The right to vote is lost in 11 states for convicted felons. The right to bear arms is also lost. Why should the non-violent lose this? Thirteen states permanently disenfranchise felons so that they may no longer vote. The Supreme Court made it harder, if not impossible, for federal courts to restore gun rights to felons who have served their time. That does not mean that the state cannot restore this right. The primary objective in the mass incarceration of Americans could be this very issue of taking away the right to have guns.

Reinstatement of the right to vote in Florida used to require an application to the Governor and could take years and still not get approved. Even now, restoration of civil rights can take fifteen years in Florida. During this time, the ex-felon cannot get many types of business licenses. That list includes: dealer's license for motor vehicles; wrecker operator; law enforcement officer, private investigator; pest control operator; many of the medical field licenses, such as nurse, therapist, paramedic, etc.; mortgage broker; title loan lender; retail installment seller; fire equipment dealer; electrical contractor, construction contractor; and numerous other licenses. So,

By Elijah Green

# The Kennel

not only can the state reduce the ex-felon to poverty with the incarceration fee, they can limit their opportunity to rise out of poverty. Add to this problem, many businesses and most government employers will not hire an ex-felon. Many businesses are reluctant to hire an ex-felon, but most states offer a tax incentive to employ an ex-felon. The federal government also offers a tax break, but usually conditions the tax incentive on the former inmate being at or below poverty level. If he owns property, there is no reason to help him till he loses it and distances himself from the middle class.

What can the female inmate expect while incarcerated and when she leaves, in addition to the possibility of the "cost of incarceration fee"? If she is married and incarcerated for one year or more, she can expect to leave divorced. The divorce rate, male & female, for inmates incarcerated a year or more is 85%. She stands a strong chance of being sexually abused.

For officers in the Federal Prison system, sexual abuse is only a misdemeanor. If she is at a private prison, sexual abuse is not against the law because the courts do not, under court definition, consider a private prison or halfway house to actually be a prison.

"Consequently, staff at contractor-owned and operated detention facilities who sexually abuse federal inmates cannot be prosecuted under federal law." If she is at a state prison, the guards will likely only receive a suspended sentence. If she reports sexual abuse and cannot prove it, she could face another year of incarceration for filing

By Elijah Green

# The Kennel

a false accusation. Intimidation and fear also prevent her from reporting. Guards sometimes trade contraband for sex. "They also are accused of threatening to plant contraband in inmates' belongings or have them transferred to other prisons farther from their families if they talked, the FBI said." She also is at perhaps a greater than 50% chance of leaving with an infectious disease. Since the law won't protect her from the staff officers, she can expect even less protection from other inmates. Why are male guards even allowed into a women's prison????? Or vice-versa? In a recent study, "female inmates had higher rates of mental health problems than their male counterparts 61 percent of females and 44 percent of males in federal prisons; 73 percent of females and 55 percent of males in state prisons; 75 percent of females and 63 percent of males in local jails."

"Studies have linked double-bunking and prison overcrowding with higher rates of stress-induced mental disorders, higher rates of aggression, and higher rates of violence." What can the male inmate expect while incarcerated and when he leaves? As mentioned above, if married and incarcerated for one year or more, the divorce rate is 85%.

Men are not exempt from sexual abuse. "Prison staff have laughed at and ignored the pleas of male prisoners seeking protection from rape by other inmates."

In July 2003, Congress passed the Prison Rape Elimination Act of 2003 to study the problem of prison rape. A commission of 9

By Elijah Green

# The Kennel

members was appointed (3 appointed by the President) and their report was due within three years of passage. In July 2006, this commission reported to congress. "It is currently anticipated that the Commission's final report will be submitted to the Congress in July, 2007." However, as of July 31, 2008, the final report has not been posted on the commission's website. Let's see, finish the job means no more traveling the country, expenses paid with per diem. Congress passing a law, or the attorney general mandating guidelines (which would then only affect federal prisons), based on this study, to help solve the problem of prison rape can wait until the commissioners finish touring the country.

The PREA of 2003 has helped some already in that grant money was also tied to the act, offering money to states that take some action to try to reduce prison rape. However, such an offer is unconstitutional, yet has become a normal method of operation for the U.S. Government. The Federal Government taxes citizens at a rate higher than necessary, then offers some of the excess tax in the form of "grants" to states which do something that Uncle Sam wants. Thereby, they are using this "grant money" to manipulate state laws and state rights. When the Prison Rape Elimination guidelines are finally issued, they will only apply to Federal Prisons once adopted, and it will be up to the states if they want to adopt these guidelines to get grant money. Each state needs to go ahead and remedy the problem within their prisons and jails and refuse the grant money. In addition, the representatives of each state should work to stop the

By Elijah Green

# The Kennel

"revenue sharing" started during the Nixon years, voting no to every piece of legislation that includes grant money.

Men and women are at a high risk of leaving prison with an infectious disease. Of inmates released from prison and jail in 1996: 1.3-1.4 million were infected with Hepatitis C; 98,000-145,000 with HIV; 39,000 with AIDS; 566,000 with Tuberculosis, Latent, while 12,000 had active TB at some point in 1996.95

Few, if any, prisons have prompt, adequate medical or dental care for inmates. Inmates with diabetes are usually limited to twice per day testing of their sugar level. This can pose a serious health risk. There is mounting evidence for vitamin D's role in preventing common cancers, autoimmune diseases, type 1 diabetes, heart disease, and osteoporosis. The body makes vitamin D when exposed to direct sunlight. Aging skin requires more sun exposure. Yet, to their own peril, many inmates, especially those in the Special Housing units, do not get to see the sun, while guards make fun of their pale complexion.

Thousands of severely ill inmates are released from the Nation's prisons and jails each year. Helping them find ways to pay for medical and mental health and living expenses is thought to be a crucial part of ensuring their successful return to the community. Some of these released inmates may be eligible for disability benefits available through Federal entitlement programs, such as Supplemental Security Income (SSI), Social Security Disability Insurance (SSDI), Medicaid,

By Elijah Green

# The Kennel

Medicare, and Veterans Pension or compensation funds." Applying for these benefits prior to release could make this assistance available immediately upon release.

In 1829, it was believed that isolating a prisoner with only a Bible and stone walls would result in the prisoner using the time to repent, pray, and find introspection, hence the name 'penitentiary'. This first experiment of solitary confinement in the United States began in Philadelphia. The practice of isolation was slowly abandoned during the following decades as many of the inmates went insane, committed suicide, or were no longer able to function in society. U.S. Supreme Court Justice Samuel Freeman Miller, in 1890, finds, "A considerable number of the prisoners fell, after even a short confinement, into a semi-fatuous condition, from which it was next to impossible to arouse them, and others became violently insane; others still, committed suicide; while those who stood the ordeal better were not generally reformed, and in most cases did not recover sufficient mental activity to be of any subsequent service to the community."

That finding being known, the question is: why has this country returned to using solitary confinement? Most prisons now have a portion of their prison dedicated to this practice, and some practice this exclusively. Because of overcrowding, there has been pressure to use the empty beds at super-max and maximum-security prisons to house non-violent inmates. Of course, the prisons don't mind, more prisoners' equal's more money.

**By Elijah Green**

# The Kennel

*"Let the children who are sent to those schools be taught to read and write... (and) above all, let both sexes be carefully instructed in the principles and obligations of the Christian religion. This is the most essential part of education. The great enemy of the salvation of man, in my opinion, never invented a more effectual means of extirpating Christianity from the world than by persuading mankind that it was improper to read the Bible at schools....*

*"The only foundation for a useful education in a republic is to be laid in religion. Without this there can be no virtue, and without virtue there can be no liberty."*

Benjamin Rush wrote this when he proposed his plan for public education in America on March 28, 1787. He also wrote,

*"By removing the Bible from schools we would be wasting so much time and money in punishing criminals and so little pains to prevent crime. Take the Bible out of our schools and there would be an explosion in crime." --Dr. Benjamin Rush, signer of the Declaration of Independence.*

## Things you can do to help:

• Remember the scripture: "All have sinned and come short of the glory of God." Therefore, be cautious how you judge another. (Matthew 7:1)

By Elijah Green

# The Kennel

- Educate your friends about jury nullification. Take time to read the Constitution and oppose those laws that infringe on the rights of Americans.

- Write letters to the editors of local newspapers and to your representatives.

- Become a pen pal with an inmate.

- Find ways to help an inmate's family - Angle Tree ministry is one way to get involved helping the children of inmates.

- Hire an ex-felon. You'll get a tax break while helping a person.

- Get involved with a prison ministry.

- Pray for the inmates.

## Pen Pal with Prisoners:

Most prisoners would love to receive mail. They are not allowed visitors except from the people who knew them prior to their incarceration. Prisons limit the number of visitors the inmate can have on his/her active visitor list to 10, 15, or 20. Frequently, loved ones sever the relationship with an incarcerated mate or friend, reducing the size of the list of potential visitors. Distance to the prison can also reduce the frequency of visits, especially if the inmate is in a private prison. Short visiting hours can also discourage friends and family

By Elijah Green

# The Kennel

from making a long trip for a short visit, as some jails limit visitation to two hours on Saturday and Sunday.

*Many inmates never get a visitor.*

There are many websites where inmates have posted ads, wanting someone to correspond with. Most sites urge caution, and recommend using a post office box address instead of the home address. Of course, if this is done, then you should also not give your last name or phone number. Prisoners are human, some good, and some bad, just like people not in prison. The Bible teaches, "All have sinned and come short of the glory of God." (Romans 3:23) And also, "If we say that we have no sin, we deceive ourselves, and the truth is not in us." (1 John 1:8)

Each state will have a site for the BOP (Bureau of Prisons) or DOC (Department of Corrections), which will have an inmate locator. By entering the inmate's name or prisoner identification number, you can learn what the person was charged with, when they were incarcerated, length of sentence, and anticipated date of parole, as well as the case number they were tried on, which could provide additional information. Many of these sites also include a photo of the inmate. Any mail must also include the prisoner identification number next to the name for him/her to receive the mail.

Quote from a female pen pal of mine: *"I'm not sure how it is in a man's prison — but at metro, it's degrading. They'll run up in your*

---

By Elijah Green

# The Kennel

*face calling you names. They'll jump on you & beat the \*\*\*\* out of you. I only weigh 109 pounds so for real, what can I do, right? If you don't have a detail, you're locked in the building all day unless you go to chow. We might get yard call at night for 30 minutes. We went to the gym last night for 10 minutes."*

Your mail could be the highlight of an inmate's day and will most likely get read several times. Will you take time to write? There are numerous websites for pen pals with inmates and you should check out several. However, www.writeaprisoner.com is perhaps the most organized site, with ideas for fun activities to include in your letters, ways to reduce recidivism, and other links.

Should you desire to give a financial gift to the prisoner's account, you should check with the prison or jail for their rules concerning adding funds to an inmate's account as these rules differ in most states. In South Dakota, for example, an inmate is allowed to spend $35 per week, must maintain $100 in a frozen account unless he is indigent or serving a life or death sentence, and "may not accumulate more than $250.00 in the savings account….. After all Disbursement Account obligations have been met, any additional monies, regardless of the source, above the $350.00 ($100.00 minimum frozen account balance plus $250.00 in savings) will stay in the inmate's frozen account until their release from custody." In other words, 100% of the funds may go to the inmates Disbursement Account.

---

By Elijah Green

# The Kennel

But, consider this: the maintenance fee that the prison pays the inmate to buy things such as stamps and envelopes, shoes, or other items from the commissary is about $5.25 per month. You could/ should check with the prison staff or chaplain to find out which inmates actually need financial help. Family of inmates is not allowed to give to another inmate's account. That is considered contraband, and the state can take 100%. In Georgia, inmates may only receive funds from family members or from friends on their visitation list. Many of the prisons also state that inmates may not receive funds from another inmate's friends, but with the incarceration rate of better than more than one in one hundred, almost everyone would know more than one inmate - www.jpay.com is a site, which can make it convenient for a fee to add funds to an inmate's account. It appears that they provide this service in 21 states.

Everyone needs to know of the love of God, including prisoners. The best way to share that with them is to experience it for yourself. You can send a gospel tract, but if you send more than one at a time it will often just be thrown away by the mailroom. Hardback books are only allowed to be received from the publisher, and not from an individual. Even when you comply with the rules, the mailroom often rejects religious literature as contraband. Stamps and money may not be mailed to an inmate. An attempt to send other forms of contraband could lead to your own incarceration.

Emmaus Correspondence School offers an excellent Bible course free to inmates. Inmates may write to:

---

**By Elijah Green**

# The Kennel

Al Stoltz, ECS Ministries
P.O. Box 1028
Dubuque, Iowa
52004-1028

to enroll in the course.  Many have come to know the Lord Jesus through this course.  Be a friend and encourage your inmate friends to sign up for the course.

Super-max Subscriptions started a program where you could trade your air miles for a gift subscription to a magazine.  They had sent a mailing to every man incarcerated at Tamms C-Max asking if they would like to receive magazine subscriptions.

"Tamms C-Max is a no contact, permanent solitary confinement prison in Southern Illinois."

Many of the inmates have been there for years with no communal activity, no phone calls, no programs, no education, no work, no librarian, and almost no reading.  Many inmates responded and are still responding to this.

By emailing to supermax@temporaryservices.org you can tell how many award miles you would like to donate.  The minimum number for the least expensive subscription is 400 miles.  They will then send you the name, inmate number and address of a prisoner(s), along with his/their subscription requests.  "You can then log in to your award

**By Elijah Green**

# The Kennel

miles account, find the page that lets you give a gift subscription, fill in the prisoner's information and send them the magazine(s) they've requested.  Note the prisoner will not see your personal information or even who gave them the subscription unless you send them a postal letter."

With over 2.3 million inmates, and 5000 prisons and jails, you could possibly start a similar program at a different institution.  Or you could get involved with a prison ministry.  Do something to make a difference!

Should a pen pal correspondence develop into a more serious relationship, understand that, statistically speaking, ex-inmates are more prone to be abusive.  Therefore, pre-marital counseling would definitely be in order if the relationship goes that far.  Also, the state can take from his assets for up to twenty years after being released.  Oops!  The Eighth Amendment is also void in the eyes of the court, as is the Fourteenth Amendment.  The other amendments to the Constitution are being infringed upon with more restrictive laws in line with Karl Marx's dream of world communism.  Many of the inmates in federal prison are there as a result of the government violating Article III of the Constitution.

The following is from the S.C. Republican Party Platform:

*"The Constitution of the United States, which established a democratic republic, provided very specific and limited powers to the*

By Elijah Green

*new government. Only those powers and duties specifically enumerated within the Constitution of the United States were granted by the States and the people, to the national government. Despite this specific limiting language of the Constitution, the Founding Fathers quickly recognized the need for further restrictive clauses. As a result, the first ten amendments to the Constitution, the Bill of Rights, were adopted. Included among these was the Tenth Amendment, which directly and articulately states, 'The powers not delegated to the United States by the Constitution, nor prohibited by it to the States, are reserved to the States respectively, or to the people.'"*

Most Republican politicians should be ashamed because of their failure to defend this party platform position vehemently!!! It won't be long before there is no right to bear arms, no freedom of speech, and no right to vote unless good people take action. Thomas Jefferson stated, "*A government big enough to give you everything you want is strong enough to take away everything you have.*"

## Other ideas for involvement and helping:

• Many families cannot afford to visit. Maybe your church or group could make this a ministry outreach. If there is a prison near you, consider a "mission" house to allow families to save hotel costs.

• Maybe you could provide transportation to and from the prison.

## Changes to the system which are needed:

By Elijah Green

# The Kennel

- Make abuse of prisoners, by prison staff, a felony, not a misdemeanor.

- Restore all of the rights of ex-felons. When their sentence is served, their punishment should end.

- Prohibit all lawmakers, law enforcement, judges, and their spouses from owning stock in prison or prison industries, or from profiting in any way from prisoners.

- Eliminate gun enhancement laws. Thousands of inmates have a 3 - 5 year extension to their sentence for a gun they lawfully owned, but was not used in any crime. (The gun was simply in the house or car.) Their enhancement portion of their sentence should be removed immediately.

- Make stiff penalties for police or prosecutors who lie on the witness stand, plant evidence, or bribe witnesses in any way, even promising "time off" for testifying.

- Legalize the possession and use of drugs, and release those inmates held solely for that charge. Provide restrictions on the sale and manufacture of drugs equal to that of alcohol and tobacco, which is to person's age 21 and older.

- Make all Federal courts stay within the guidelines of Article III of the U.S. Constitution.

---

By Elijah Green

# The Kennel

• Require all prisoners to be housed within 100 miles of where they were tried. This would place the majority of inmates within reasonable visiting distance of their family. The idea that a prisoner can be shipped over a thousand miles, yet claim the prison policy encourages family visitation to promote the inmate's mental health is absurd!

• Allow conjugal visits for married inmates and their spouses.

• Don't allow male guards at women's prisons, or vice versa.

• Increase the use of home confinement as an alternative to prison.

• Make prison industries comply with OSHA regulations.

• Make the Food & Drug laws also applicable to prisons.

• Make the government comply with age discrimination laws instead of allowing exceptions to the law.

• Abandon the use of private prisons.

• Write your representatives to make the telephone providers reduce their rates to prisons.

• Provide better visiting areas, with activities for the children. (i.e. playground, toys, games, books.)

By Elijah Green

# The Kennel

• Encourage your representatives to seek alternatives to incarceration. Provide your suggestions. Remember, in God's perfect laws, which man still could not keep, no provision was made for incarceration. The punishment was to kill, whip, or fine the offender.

• Whereas the right to a speedy trial is constantly ignored, require that, from the time of being charged, the prosecution has a maximum of 90 days to bring the case to trial with the only delays allowed to be those requested by the defense attorneys. Also, require that 72 hours be the maximum a person can be detained without being charged.

• Stop the incarceration fee immediately. The goal should be to "rehabilitate" the offender, not bring him/her down to poverty along with their family.

• Abolish medical experiments on prisoners.

• Allow furloughs for all non-violent inmates.

102

# The Kennel

## Thoughts & Questions For Further Discussion:

1. Suppose you were called for jury duty and the defendant was charged with armed robbery, and possession of a weapon. Would you recognize that armed robbery already assumes the possession of a weapon, and that the charge of possession of a weapon is an infringement of the Constitutional Amendments? As a juror, you could find guilty, if the evidence supported guilt, of the armed robbery while voting not guilty of the possession of a weapon, since this is double jeopardy.

2. Suppose that in the above case, the accused is also charged with possession of a controlled substance. You could recognize that this is a bad law, practice jury nullification, and vote Not Guilty on this charge.

3. Other countries, Norway, Japan, Britain, Germany, Australia, Ireland, etc. Have much lower incarceration rates and lower crime rates. Why?

**By Elijah Green**

# The Kennel

## Comments From Prisoners:

*"I never would have believed how bad our justice system is just six months ago. This book tells the truth!" –David*

*"Great book! Only draw-back: we are treated worse than dogs." – Justin*

*"I read it three times and wept each time. It's so true!" –Kenny*

*"Please send this to my congressman! He has the power to fix this and doesn't have a clue there is even a problem." –Jeff*

*"My wife left me when I had been in for a year. I lost my job and my house. My children have gone wild; all because of Rule "Two drug dealers in prison testified that I sold them drugs. I've never*

By Elijah Green

# The Kennel

*met either one and never sold or used drugs in my life, but they got time off and I got four years. Please help fix this evil system!" – Gary*

www.law.ku.edu/research-study-guides

For a Complete Resource Guide of The Kennel visit us on the Web at

## www.2peter3.com

For DVDs, Books, Blog and to Seminar Events Go To:
2Peter3.com **or** DrDino.com
**or** Call: 1 (855) BIG DINO (244-3466)
**Follow On Social Media**
**Search:** Kent Hovind Official
29 Cummings Road Pensacola FL 32503

---

**By Elijah Green**